LANGUAGE
for
THINKING

Siegfried Engelmann • Jean Osborn

WORKBOOK

A Division of The McGraw·Hill Companies

Columbus, Ohio

www.sra4kids.com

SRA/McGraw-Hill

A Division of The **McGraw·Hill** *Companies*

Send all inquiries to:
SRA/McGraw-Hill
8787 Orion Place
Columbus, OH 43240-4027

Printed in the United States of America.

ISBN 0-02-684888-0

23 24 25 26 LOV 22 21 20

Name _____

Lesson 6

Name _____

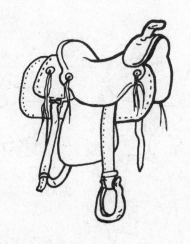

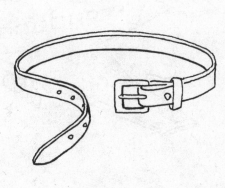

Lesson 6

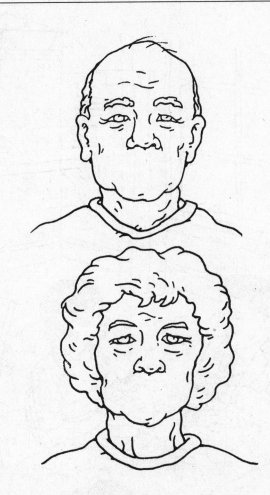
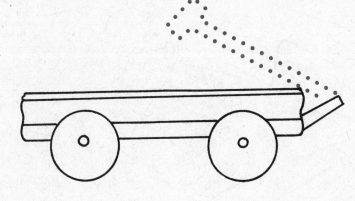
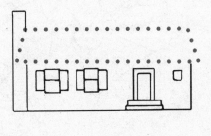

Name _____

Lesson 8   Name _____

Name _____

Lesson 9

Name _____

Lesson 10

Name _____

Lesson 10   Name _____

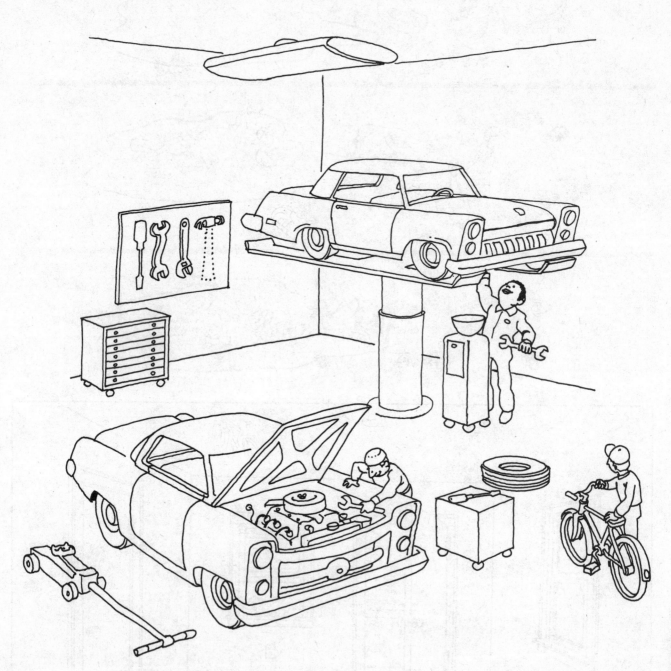

Lesson 11

Name _____

Lesson 11

Name _____

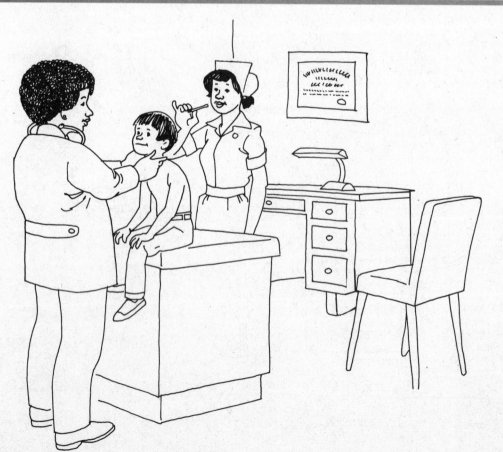

CEREAL

Lesson 13

Name _____

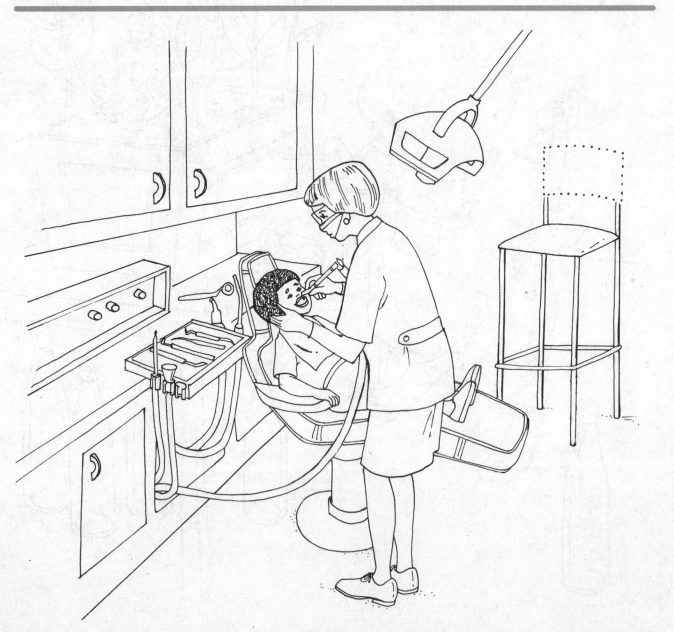

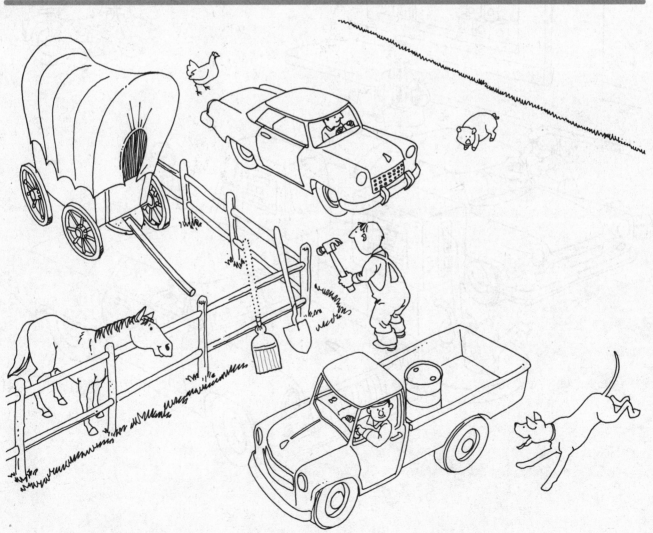

Lesson 15

Name _____

Lesson 16

Name _____

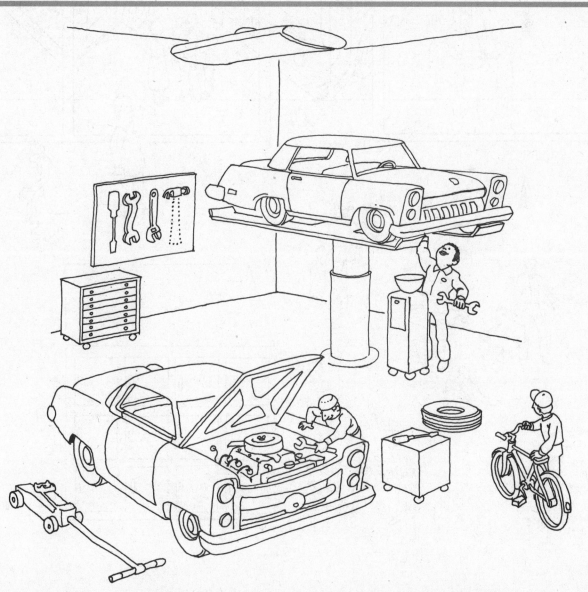

Name _____

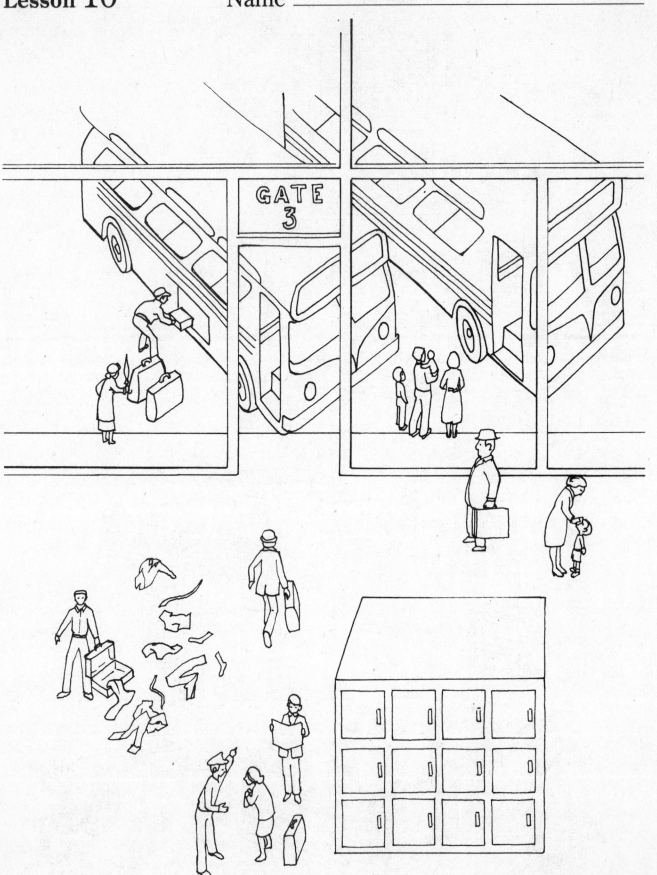

GATE
3

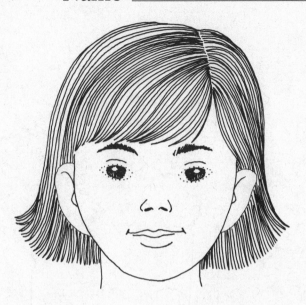

Lesson 17 Name _____

Lesson 18

Name _____

VEGETABLES & FRUIT

Lesson 19

Name _____

Name _____

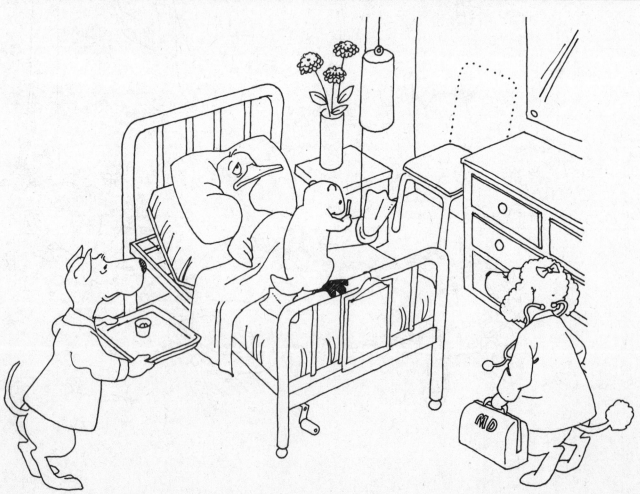

Name _____

Lesson 22

Name _____

Name _____

Lesson 23   Name _____

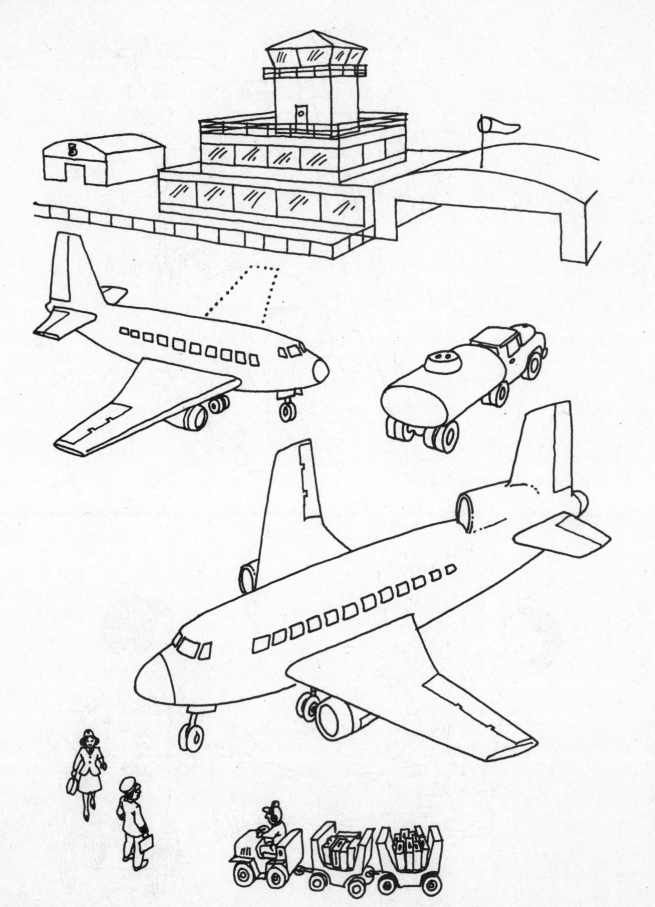

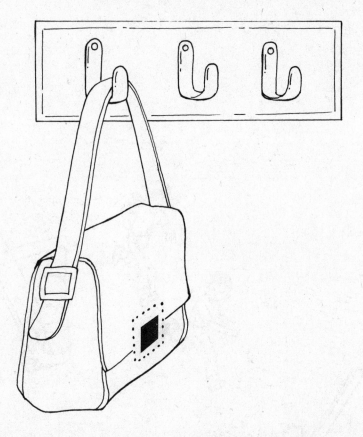

Name _____

Lesson 26

Name _____

Name _____

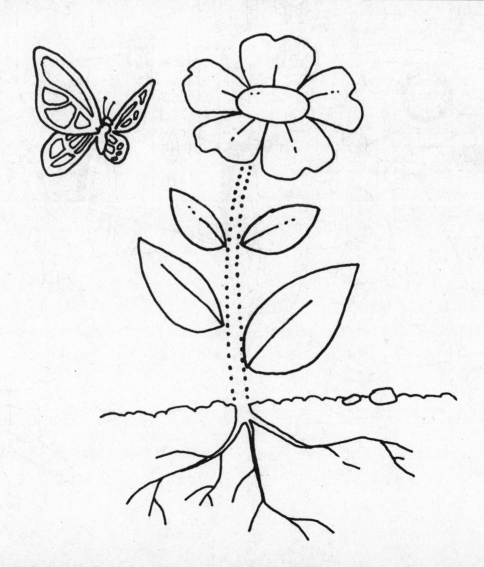

Name _____

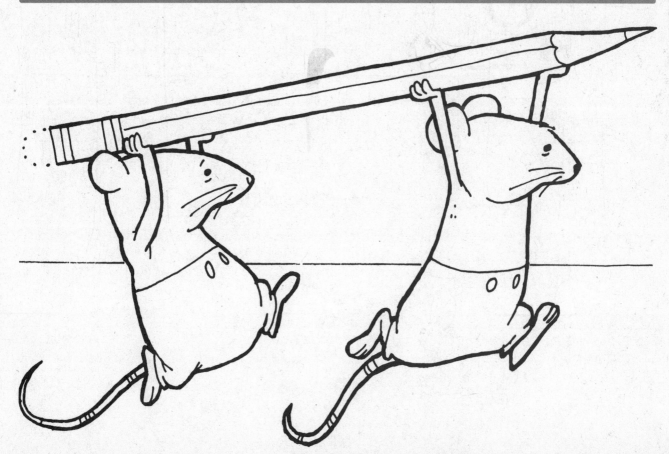

Name _____

Lesson 32

Name <u>Oisin</u>

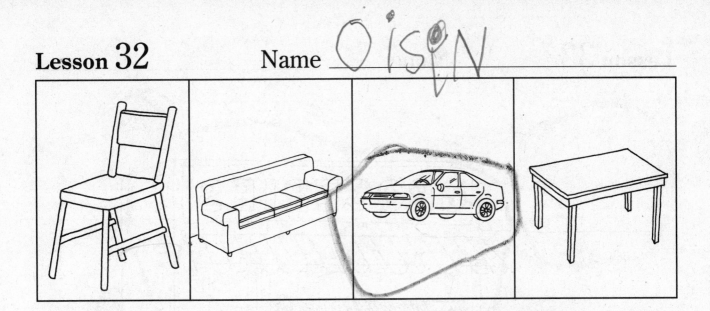

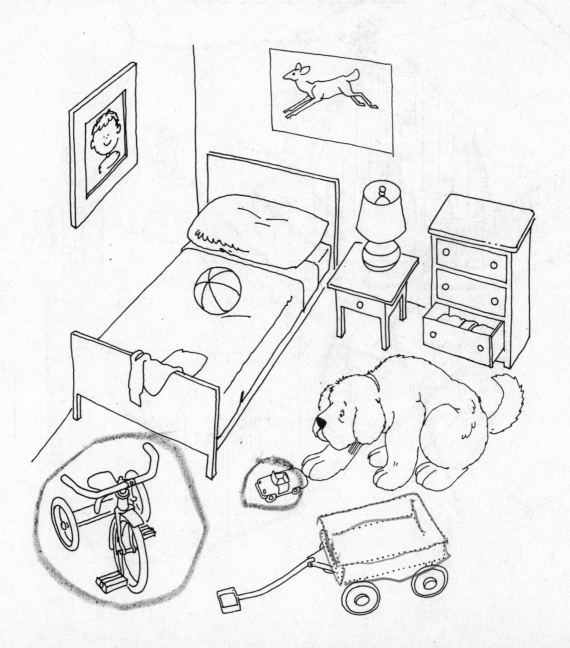

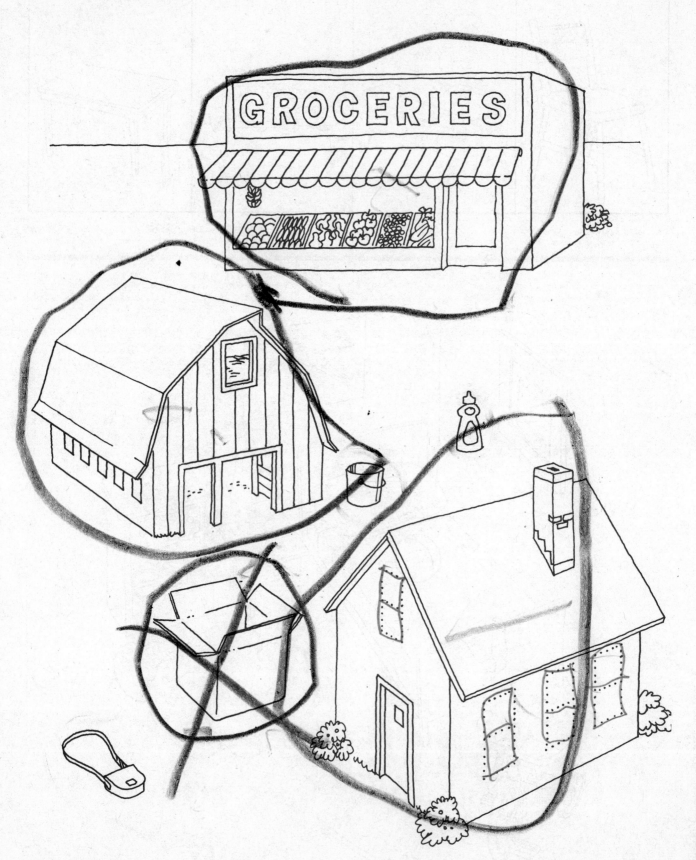

Lesson 33   Name _____

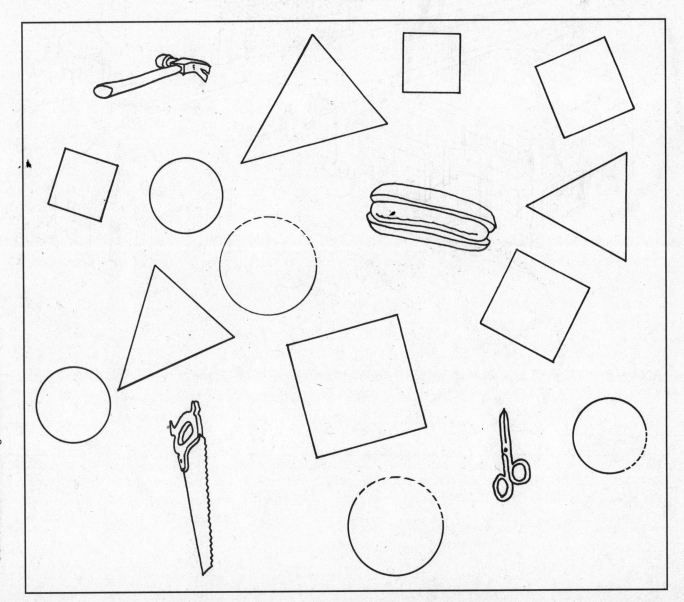

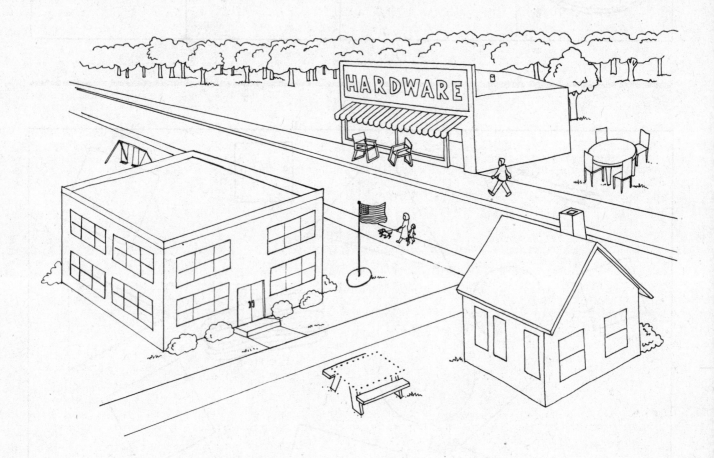

Name _____

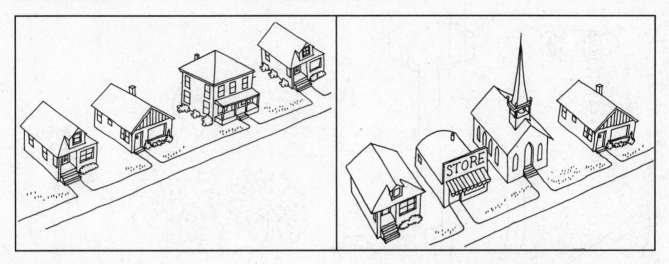

Name _____

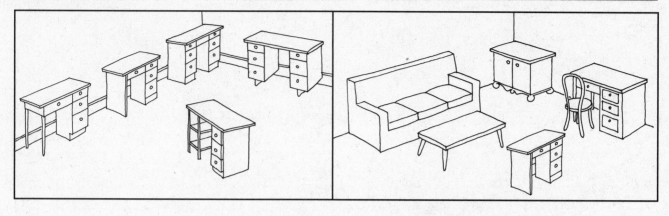

Name _____

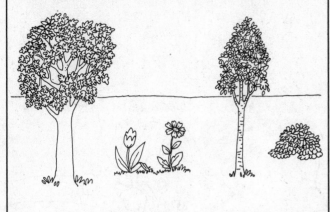
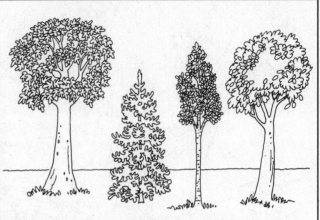

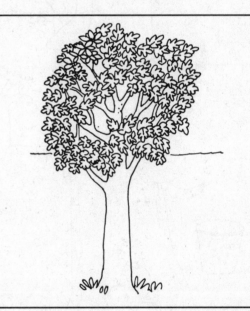

Name _____

Name _____

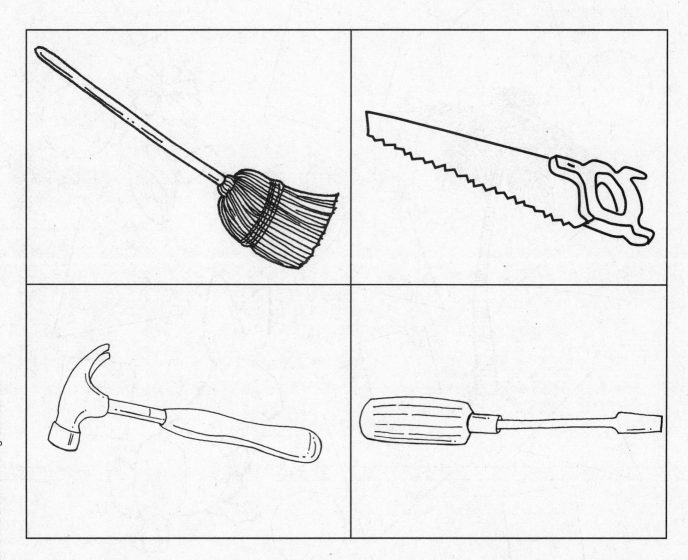

Name _____

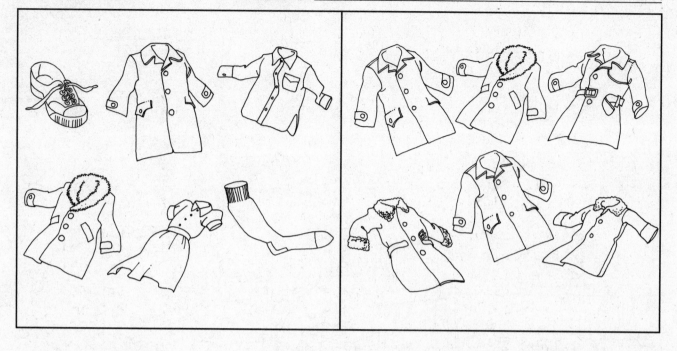

Name _____

Name _____

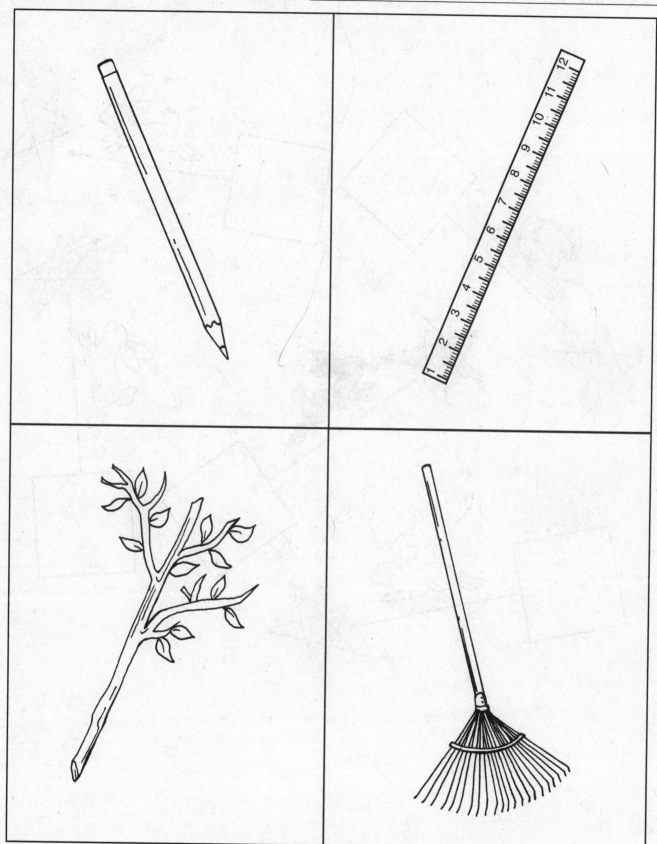

Lesson 41   Name _____

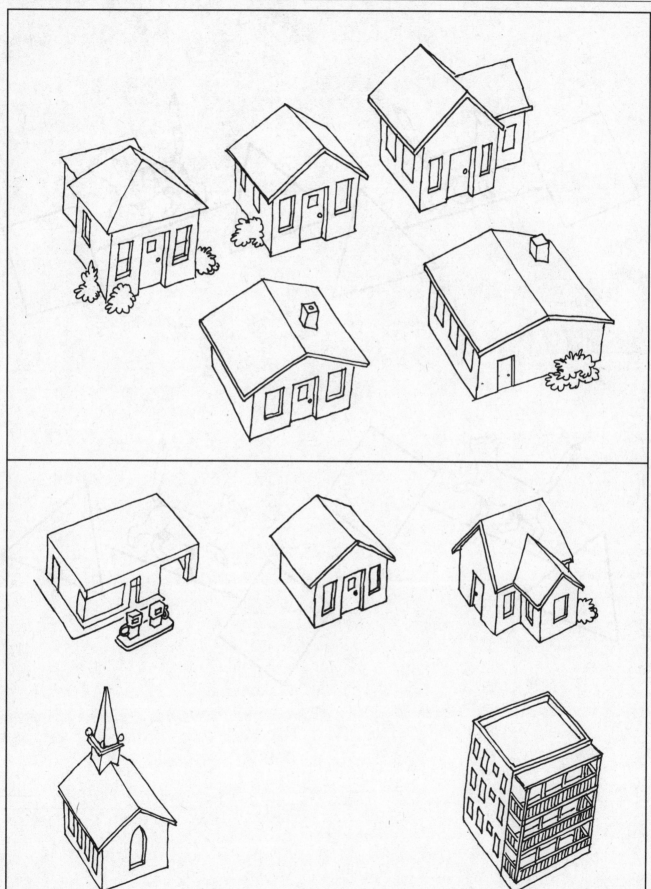

Name _____

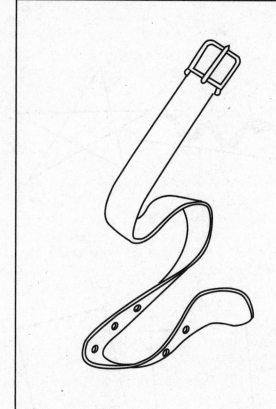

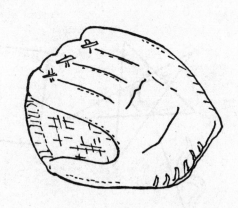

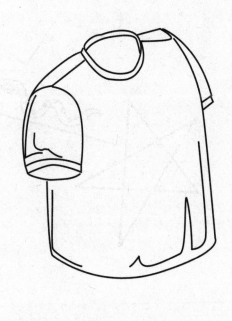

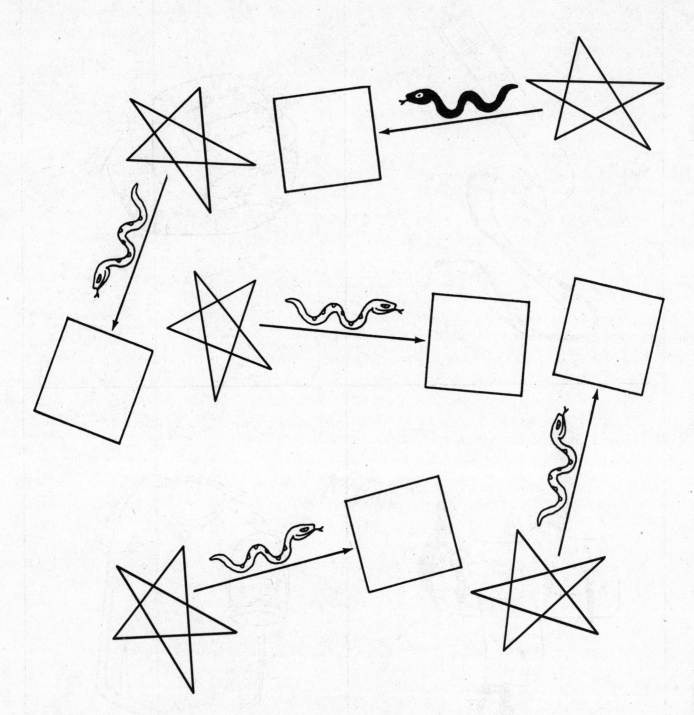

Name _____

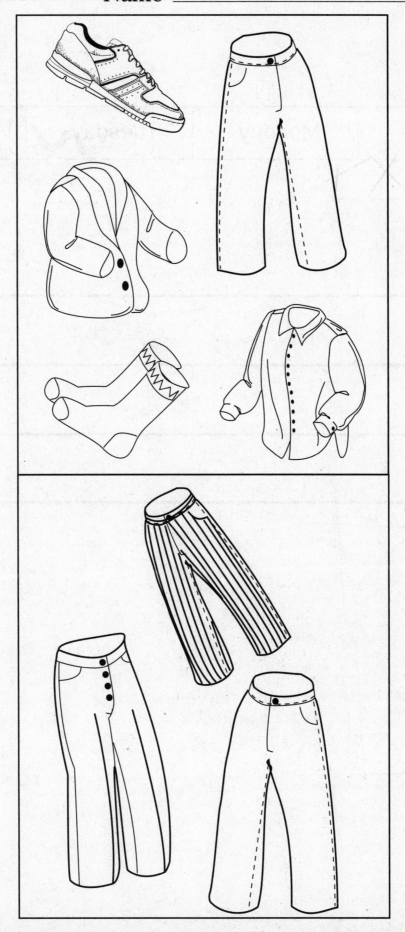

Lesson 44

Name _____

Sunday	Monday	Tuesday	Wednesday

Lesson 45　　　Name _____

Sunday	Monday	Tuesday	Wednesday

_____

_____

_____

_____

Lesson 46

Name _____

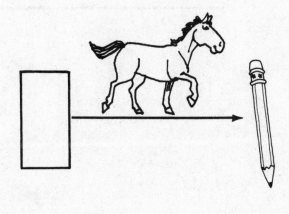

Lesson 46

Name _____

Thursday	Friday	Saturday

_____

_____

_____

Lesson 47   Name _____

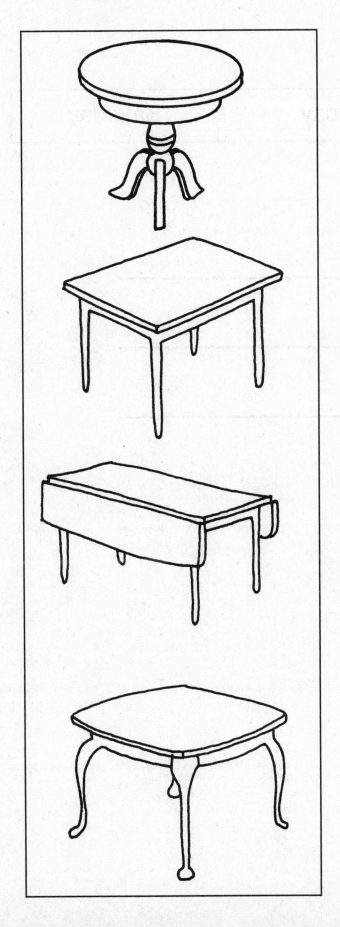

Lesson 47

Lesson 47

Thursday	Friday	Saturday

_____

_____

_____

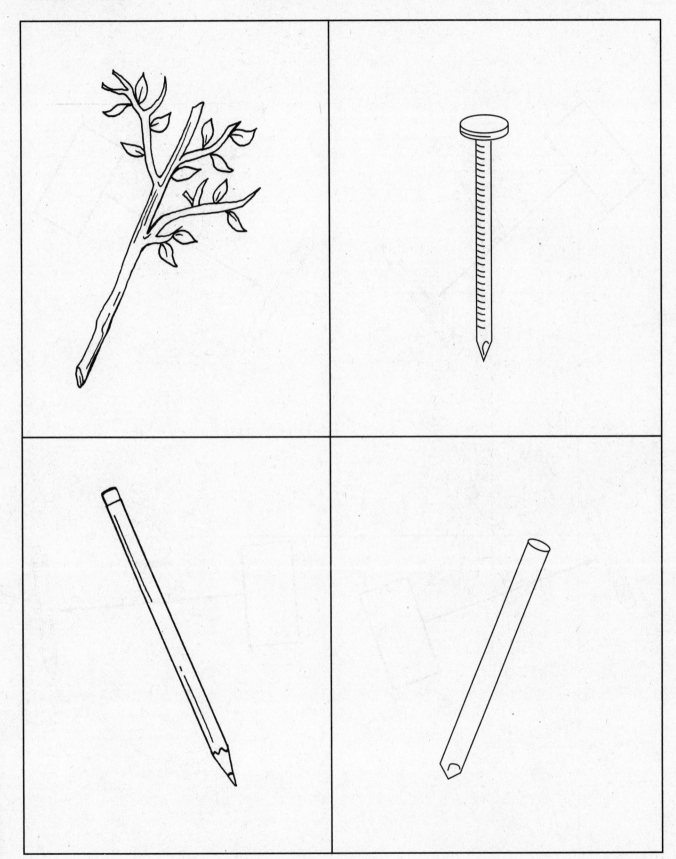

Name _____

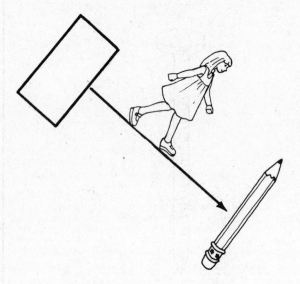

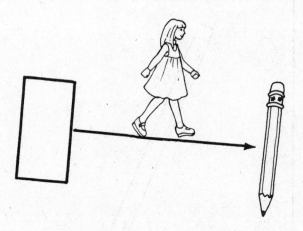

Lesson 49

Name _____

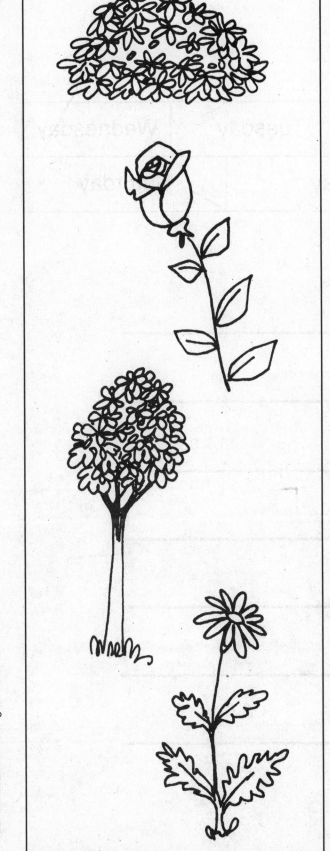

Name _____

Sunday	Monday	Tuesday	Wednesday
Thursday		Friday	Saturday

_____

_____

_____

_____

_____

_____

_____

Lesson 50

Name _____

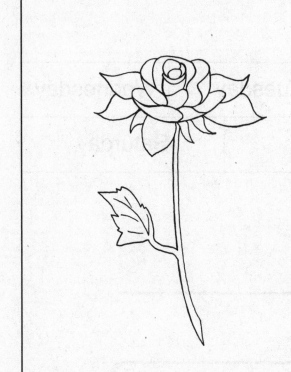

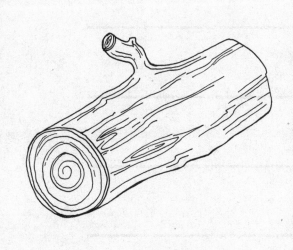

Lesson 50

Lesson 50

Name _____

Sunday	Monday	Tuesday	Wednesday
Thursday		Friday	Saturday

_____

_____

_____

_____

_____

_____

Lesson 52

Name _____

Lesson 52

Name _____

Sunday	Monday	Tuesday	Wednesday
Thursday		Friday	Saturday

_____

_____

_____

_____

_____

_____

Name _____

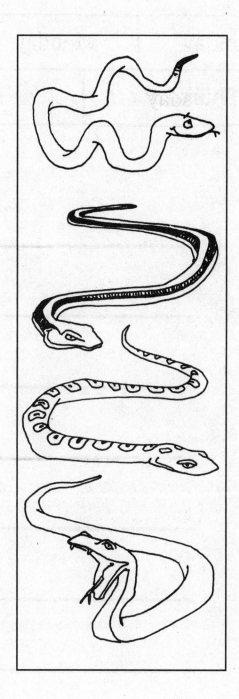

Lesson 53

Name _____

Sunday	Monday	Tuesday	Wednesday
Thursday		Friday	Saturday

_____

_____

_____

_____

_____

_____

_____

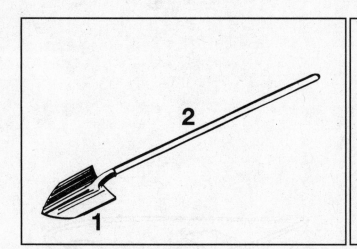

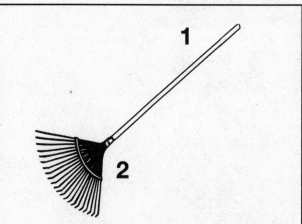

shovel   rake

_____   _____

Lesson 54

Name _____

Name _____

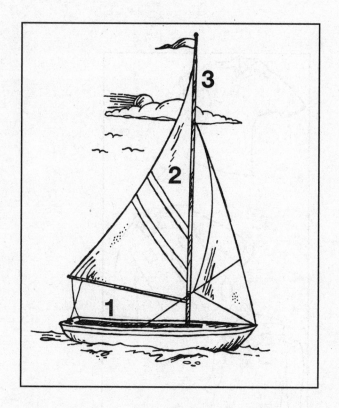

sailboat

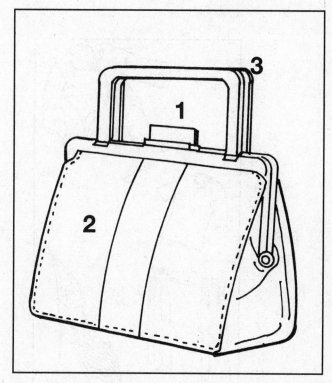

purse

Lesson 55

Name _____

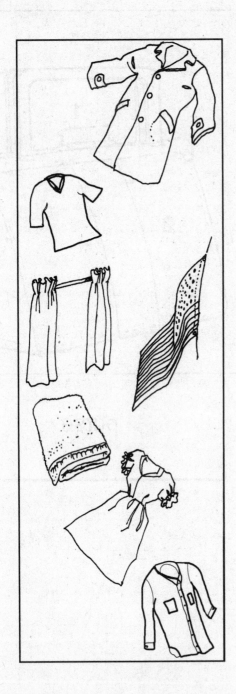

Name _____

Name _____

Sunday	Monday	Tuesday	Wednesday
Thursday	Friday		Saturday

_____

_____

_____

_____

_____

_____

_____

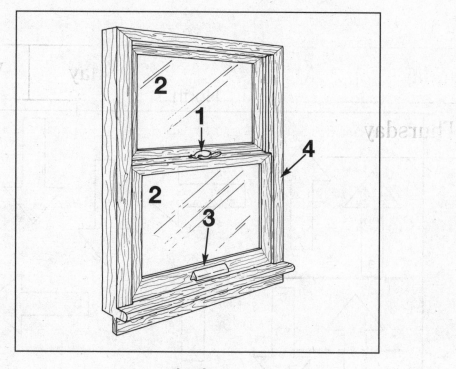

window

_____

Lesson 57

Name _____

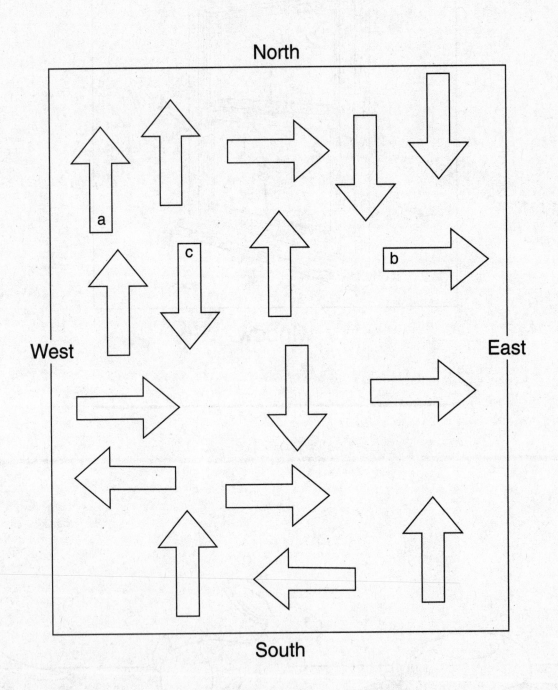

Lesson 58

Name _____

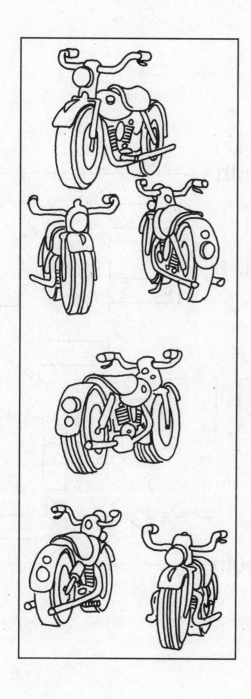

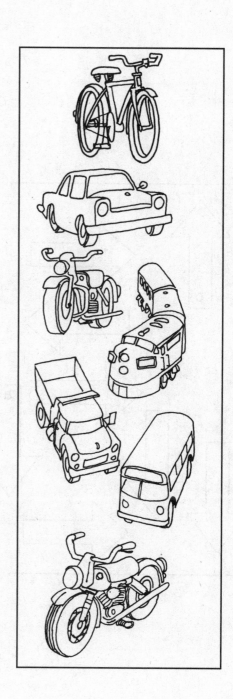

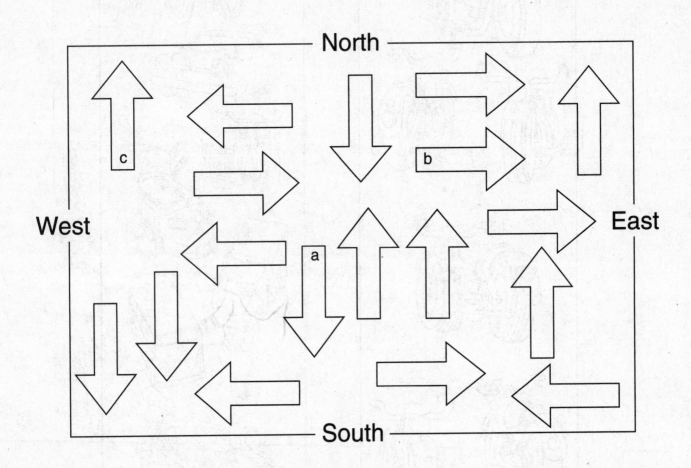

Name _____

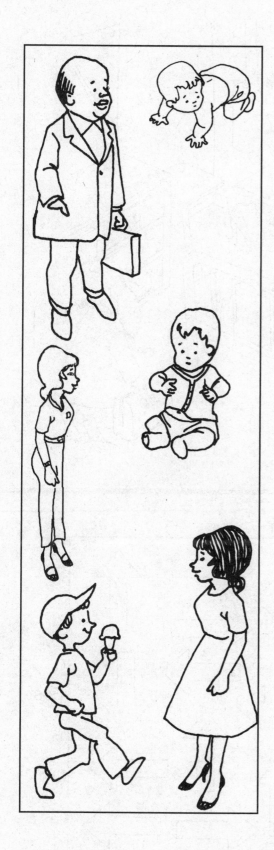

Name _____

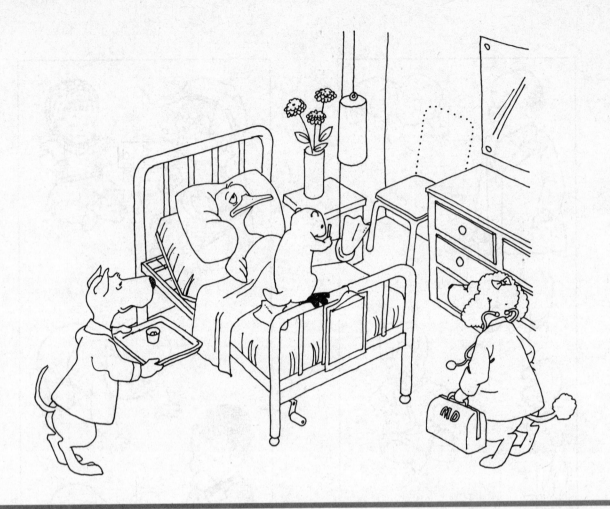

North

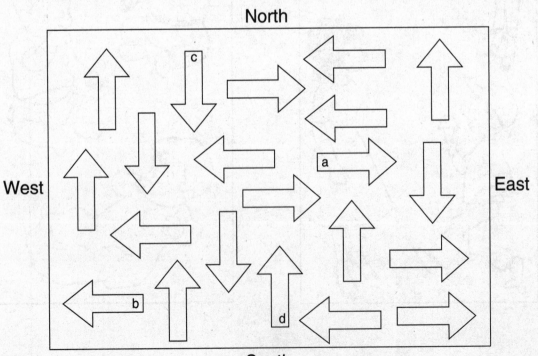

West

East

South

Lesson 60

Name _____

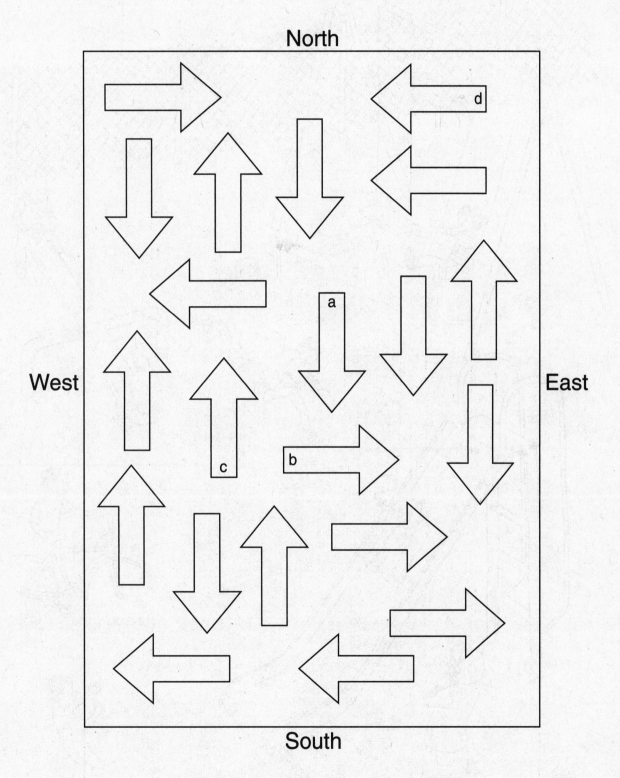

North

West

East

South

Name _____

Name _____

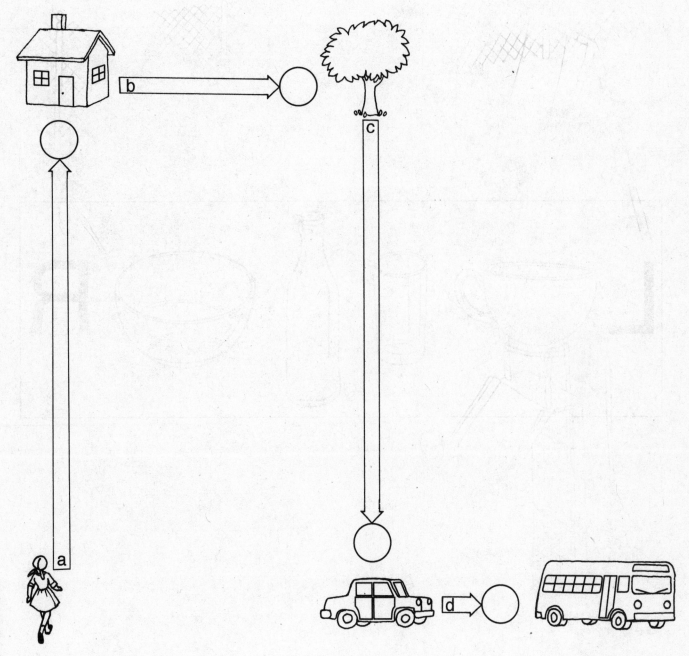

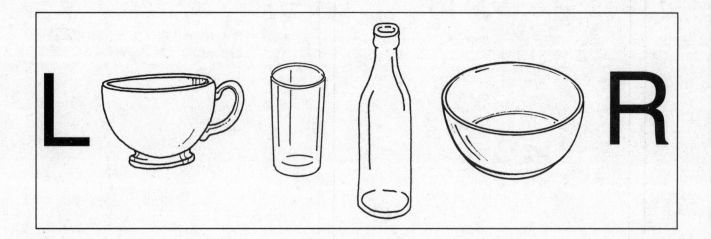

Name _____

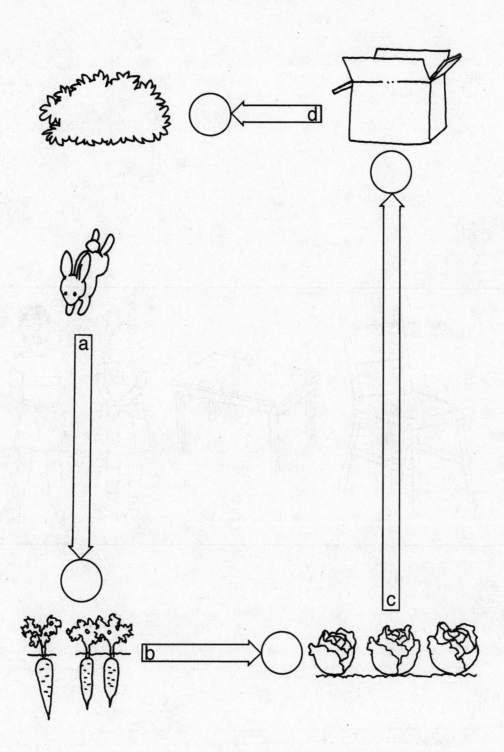

Lesson 62

Name _____

L   R

Name _____

Name _____

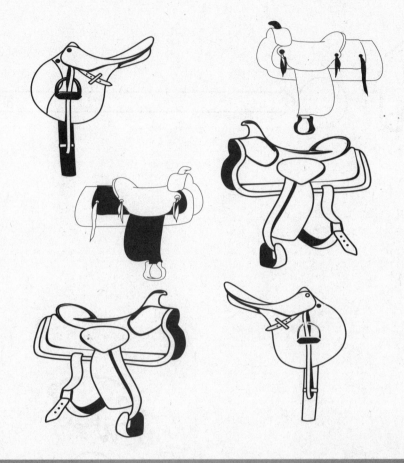

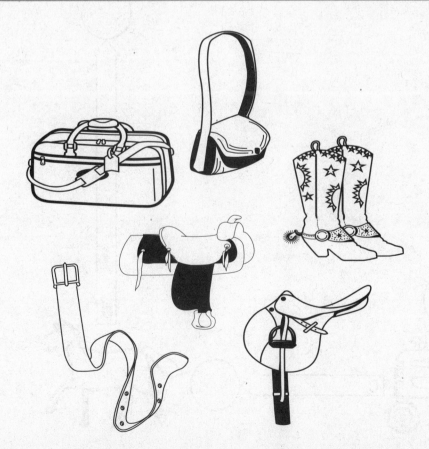

Lesson 64   Name _____

Name _____

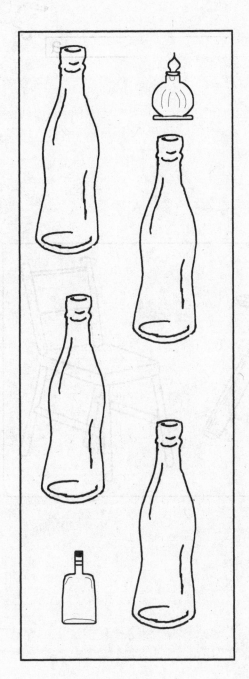
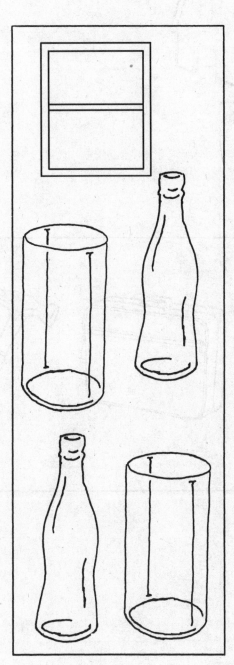

Name _____

Lesson 66

Name _____

Lesson 66   Name _____

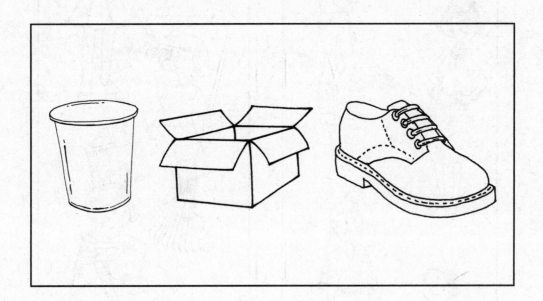

Name _____

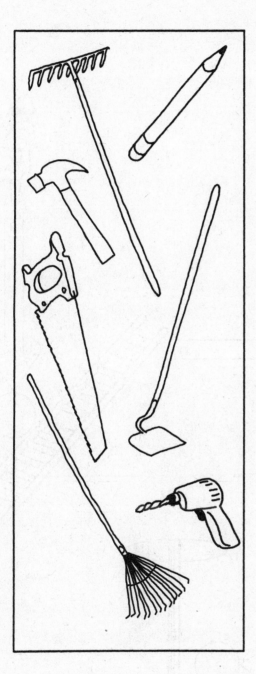

Lesson 67

Name _____

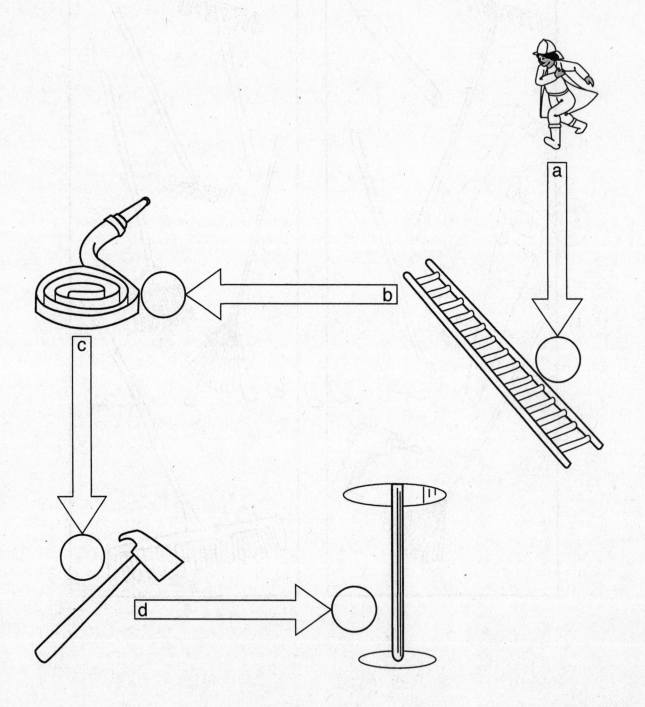

Name _____

Name _____

Lesson 69

Name _____

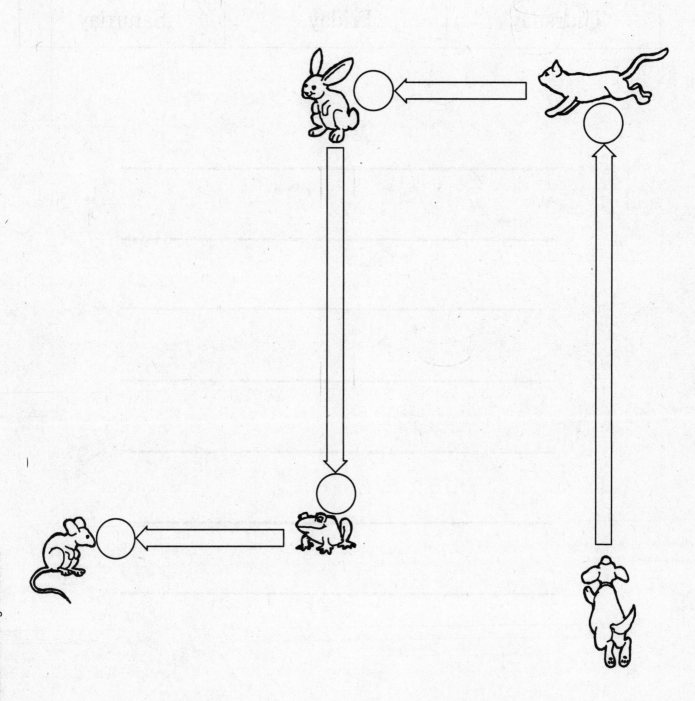

Lesson 69

Name _____

Sunday	Monday	Tuesday	Wednesday
Thursday		Friday	Saturday

_____

_____

_____

_____

_____

_____

_____

Name _____

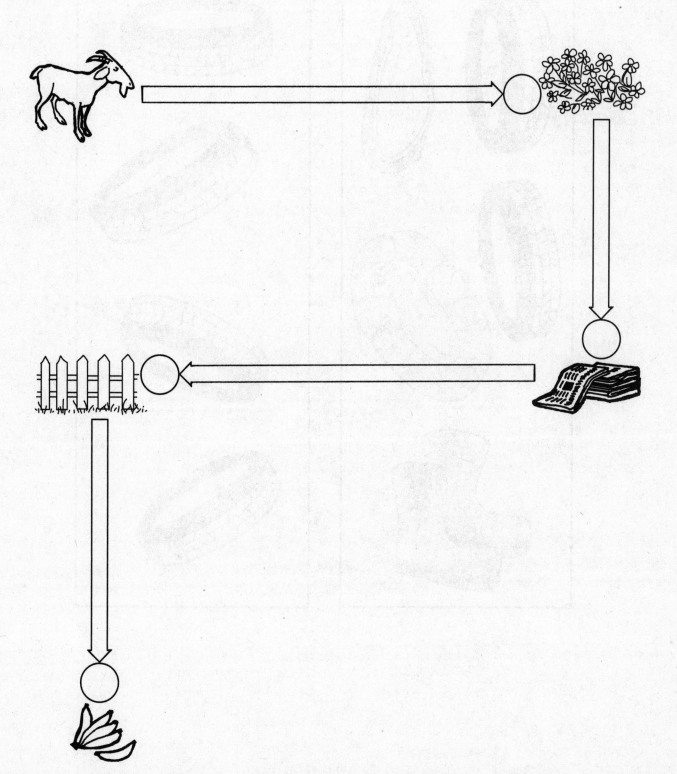

Name _____

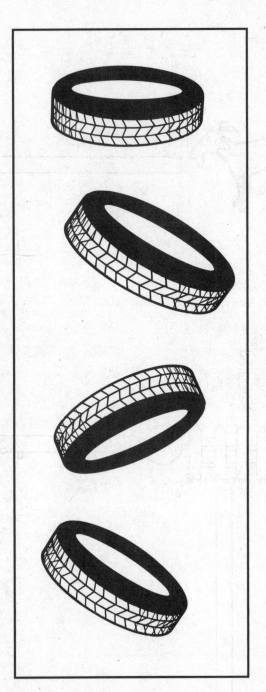

Name _____

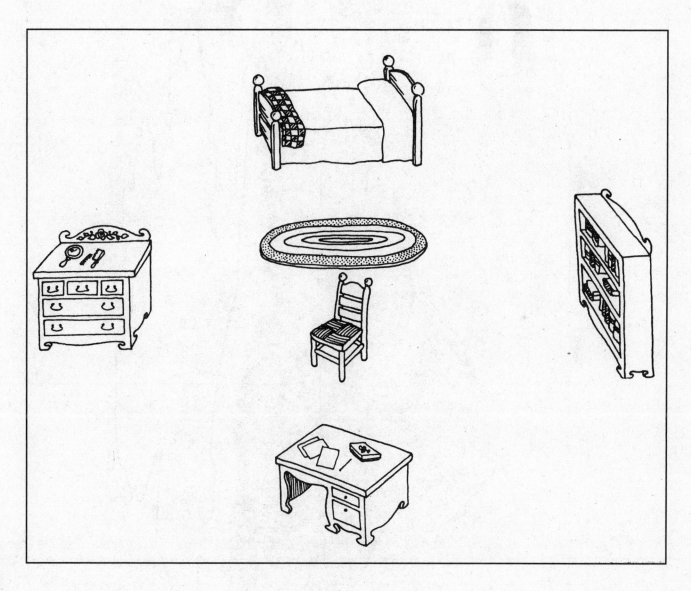

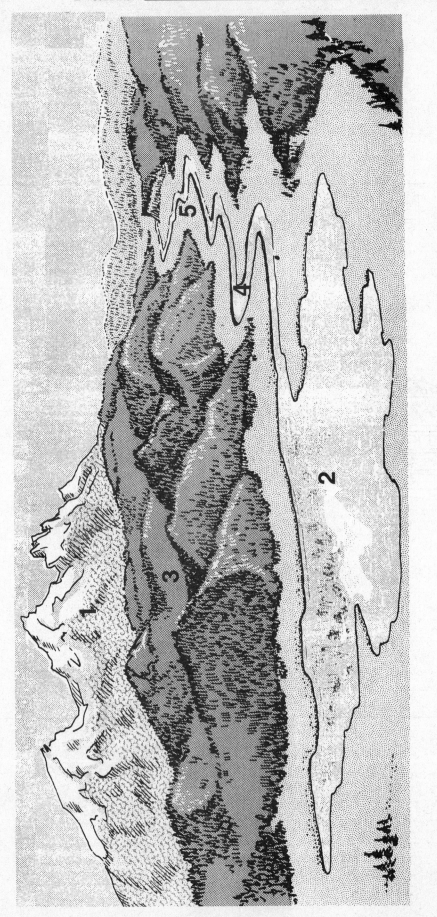

Name _____

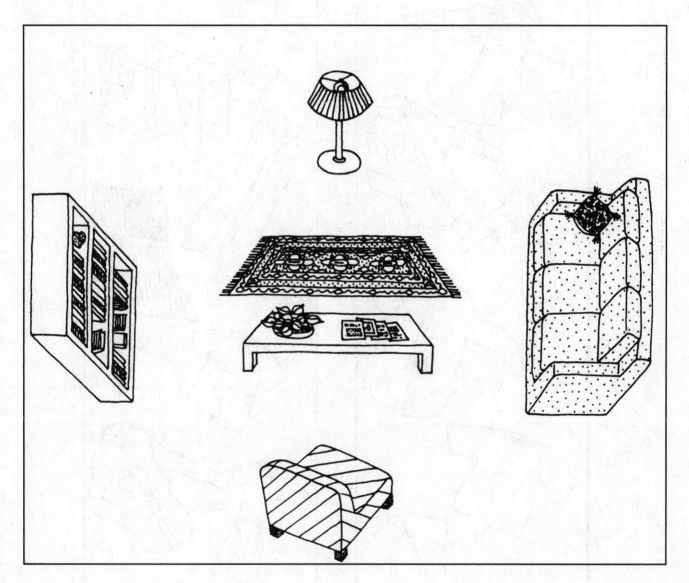

Name _____

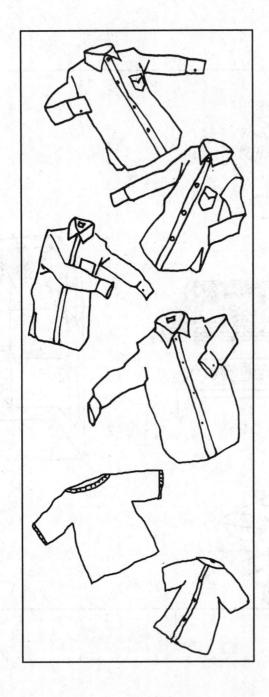

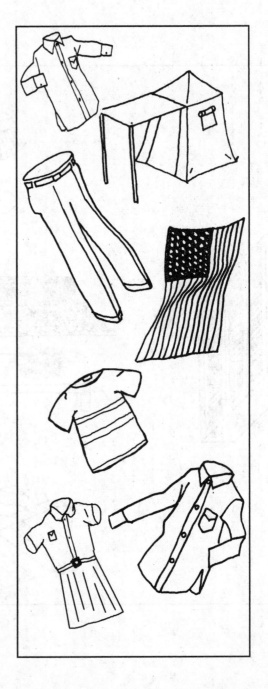

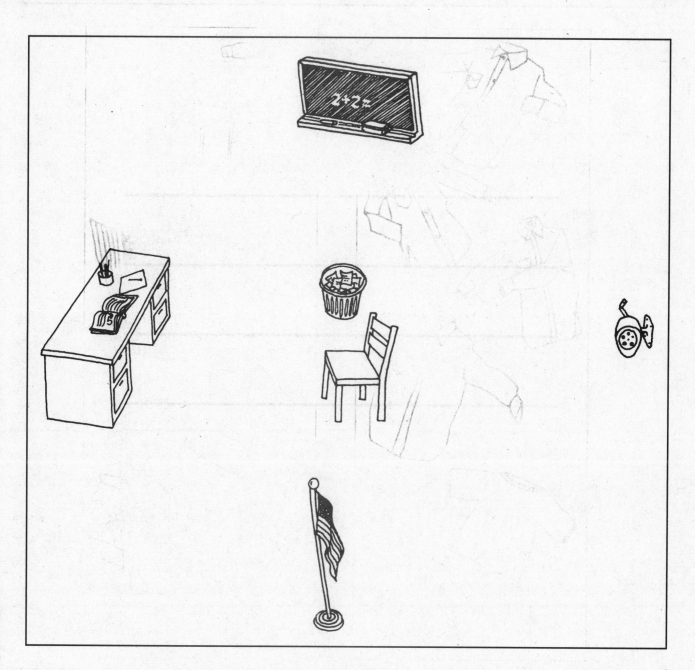

winter	spring	summer	fall

_____

_____

_____

_____

Lesson 74   Name _____

Name _____

winter	spring	summer	fall

_____

_____

_____

_____

Name _____

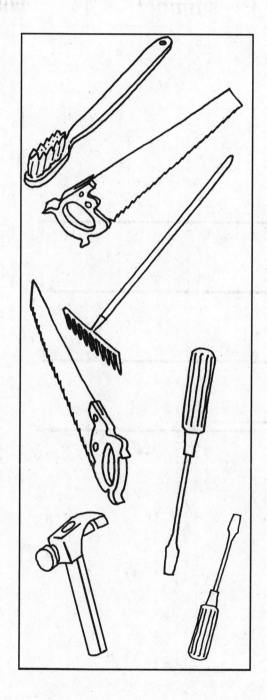

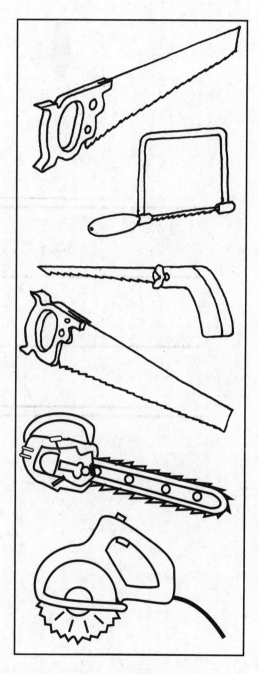

winter	spring	summer	fall

Name _____

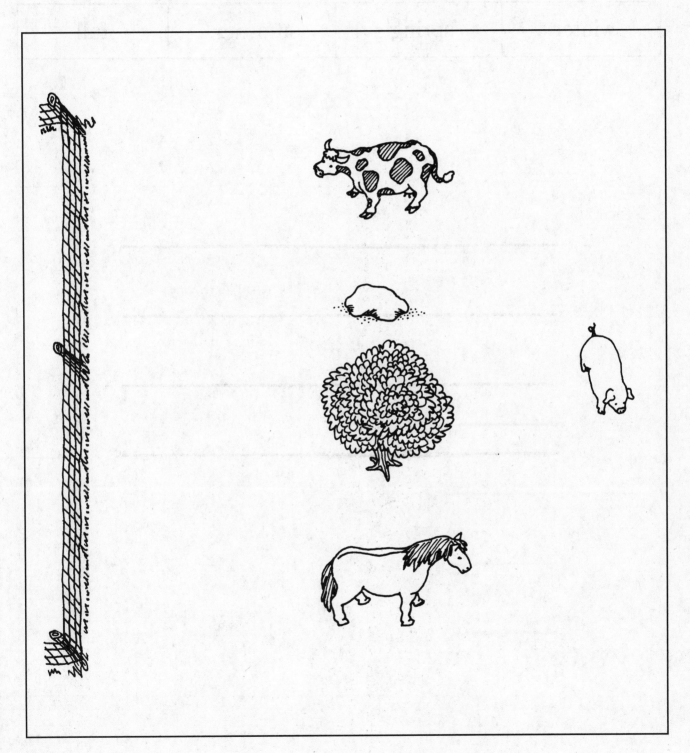

Lesson 76   Name _____

winter	spring	summer	fall

_____

_____

_____

_____

Name _____

Name _____

Lesson 78

Name _____

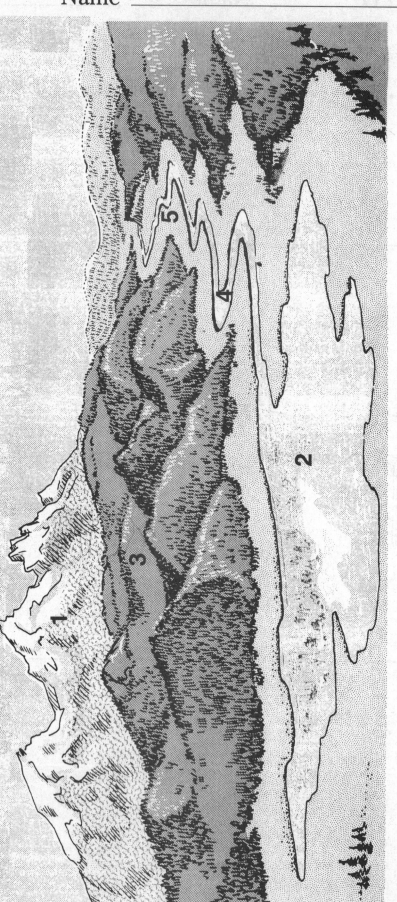

Name _____

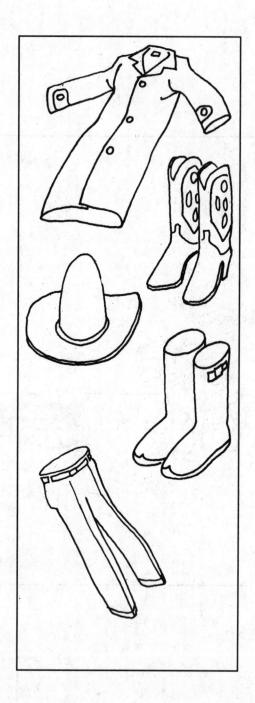 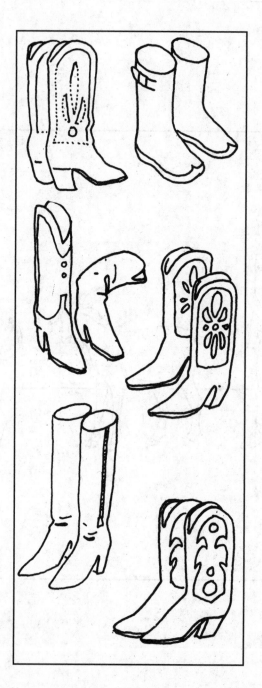

Lesson 80

Name _____

Name _____

winter	spring	summer	fall

_____

_____

_____

_____

Lesson 81

Name _____

Name _____

has   **as**   has

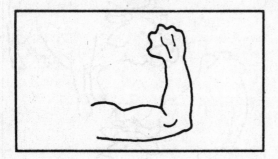

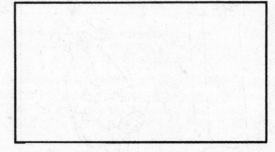

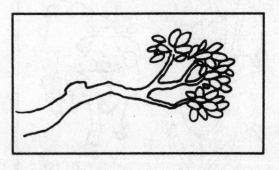

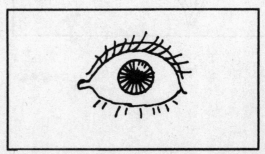

Lesson 82

Name _____

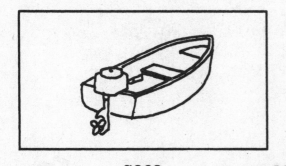

goes **as** goes

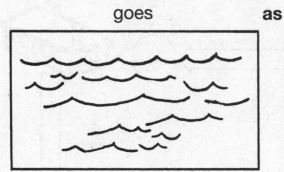

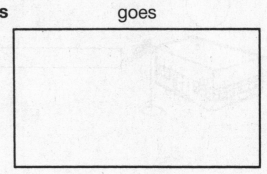

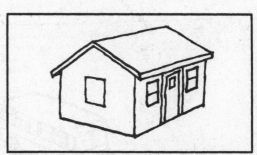

Lesson 82

Name _____

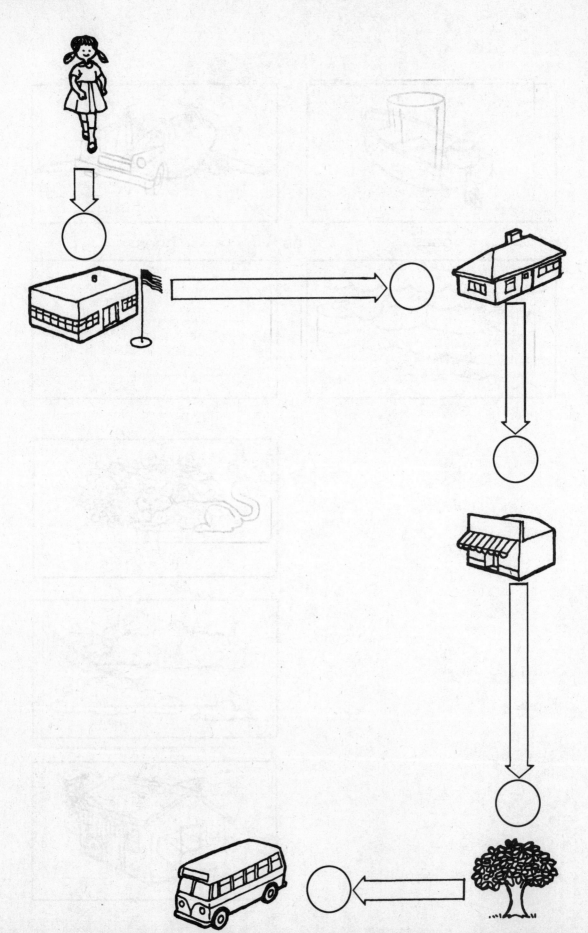

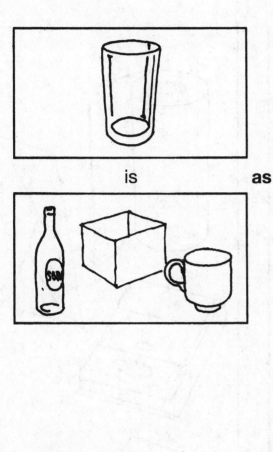

is   **as**   is

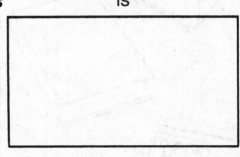

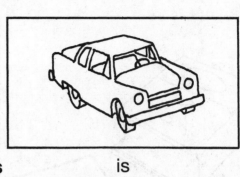

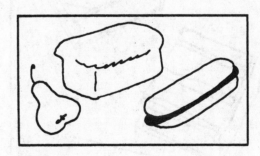

Lesson 84　　Name _____

winter	spring	summer	fall

_____

_____

_____

_____

Name _____

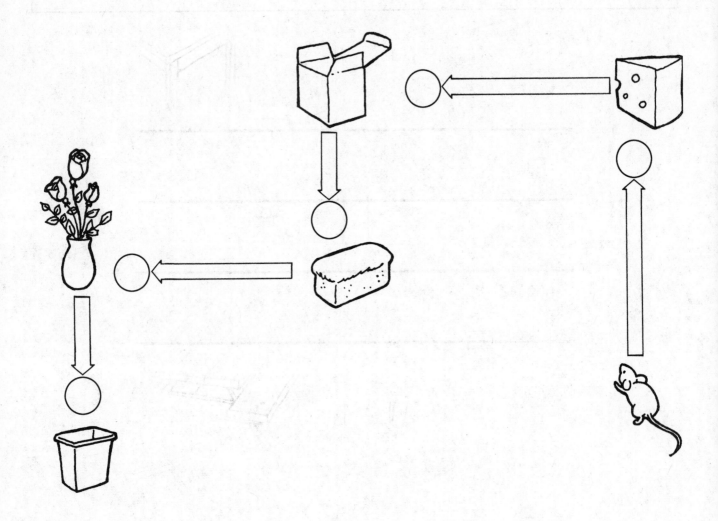

Name _____

Lesson 85

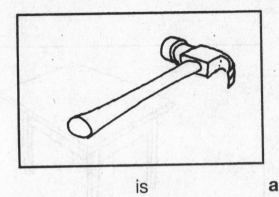

is   **as**   is

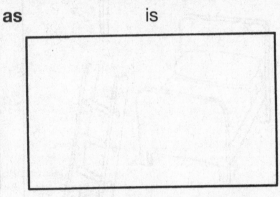

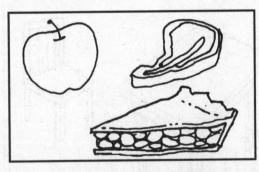

Name _____

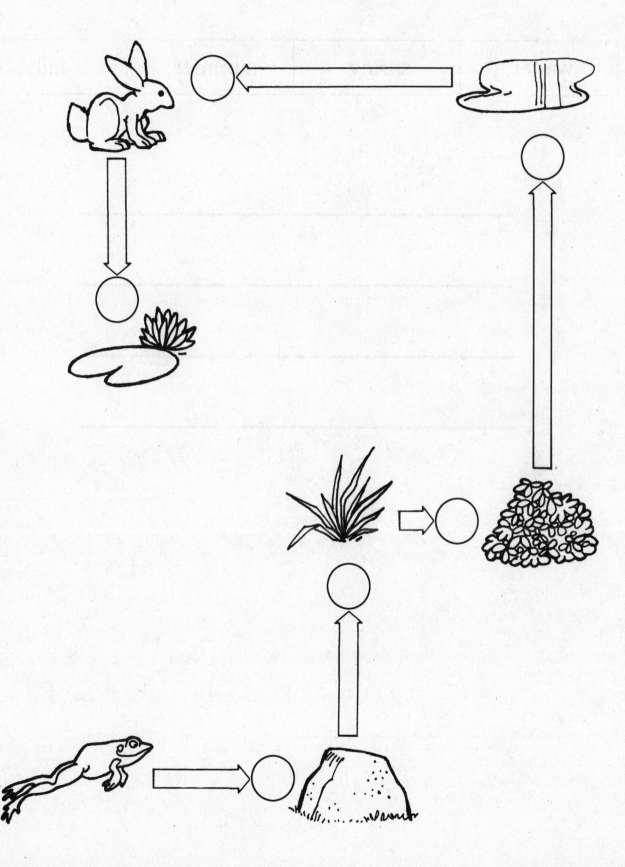

Lesson 86

winter	spring	summer	fall

_____

_____

_____

_____

Lesson 87   Name _____

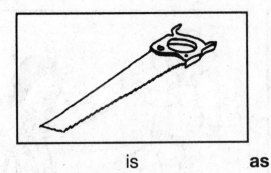   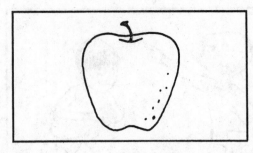

is   **as**   is

   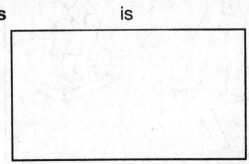

Lesson 88

Name _____

Sunday	Monday	Tuesday	Wednesday
Thursday		Friday	Saturday

_____

_____

_____

_____

_____

_____

Name _____

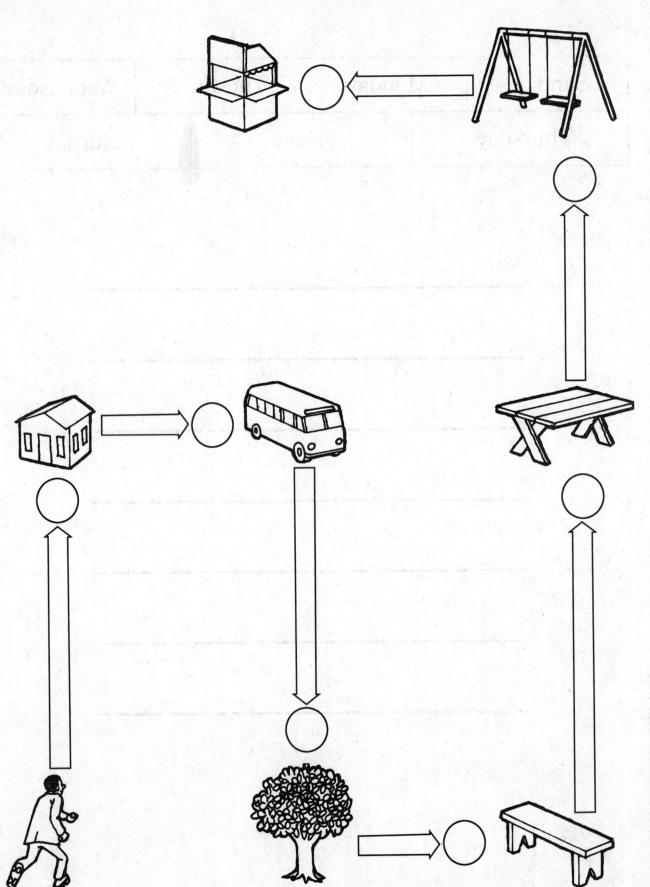

Name _____

Lesson 89

Name _____

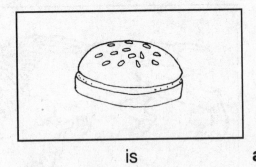 

is   **as**   is

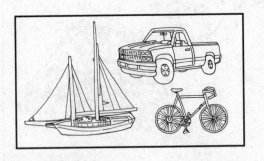

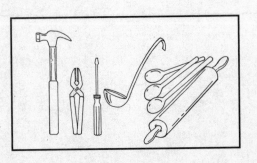

Name _____

tools	plants

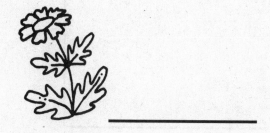 _____

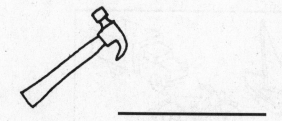 _____

Name _____

is   as   is

 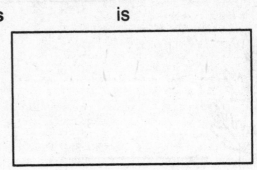

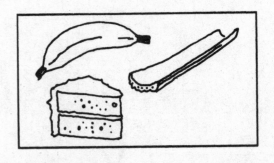

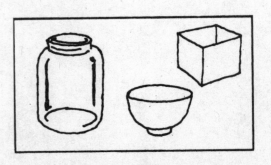

Lesson 91   Name _JAYDENM_

food	vehicles

 _venikles_

 _food_

 _food_

 venikles

 is

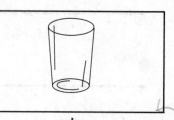

as

 is

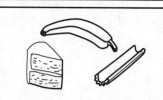

Lesson 91   Name __JAYDENN__

Sunday	Monday	Tuesday	Wednesday
Thursday		Friday	Saturday

TODAY'S

Monday

_____

_____

_____

_____

_____

_____

Name

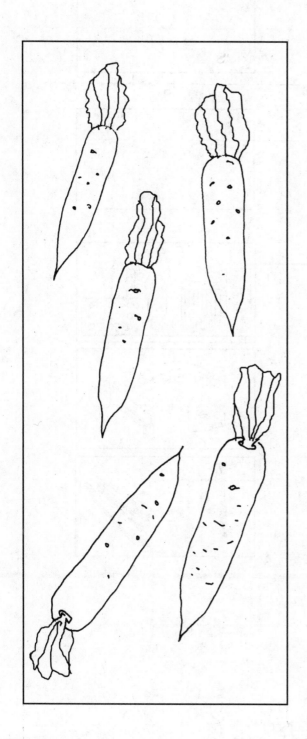

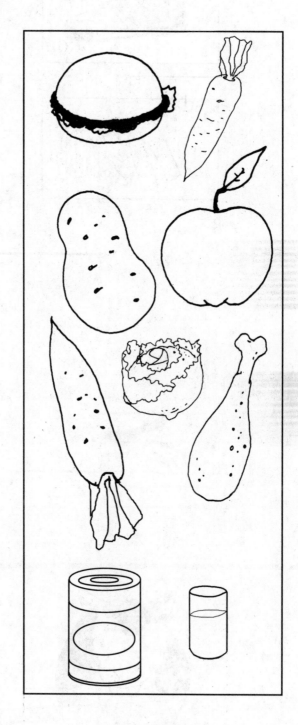

is   **as**   is

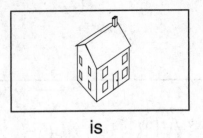

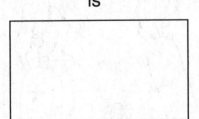

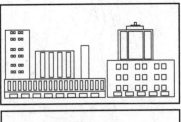

Name _____

animals	clothing

_____

_____

_____

Name _____

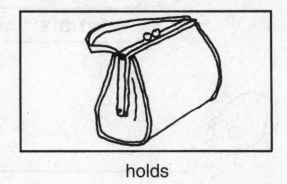

holds   **as**   holds

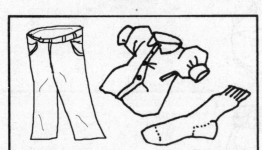

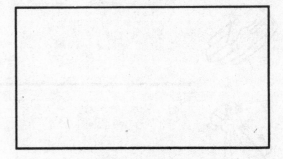

Lesson 94   Name _____

△ | **rough**   **tall**   **old**   **pull** |

1. push _____   3. smooth _____

2. young _____   4. short _____

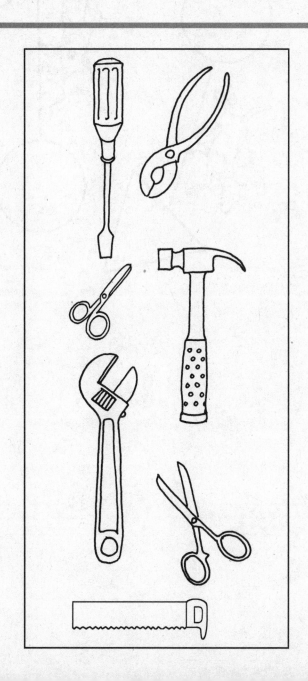 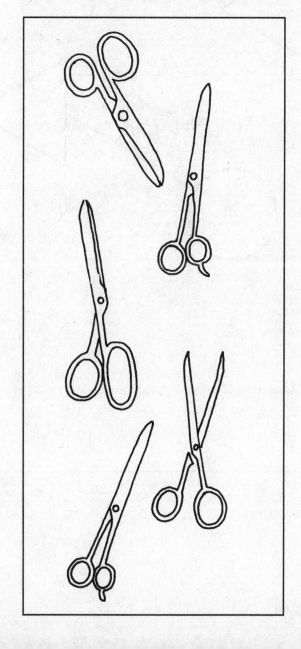

Lesson 94   Name _____

Lesson 95

Name _____

△ | **win** **dry** **short** **fast** |

1. slow _____

3. wet _____

2. lose _____

4. tall _____

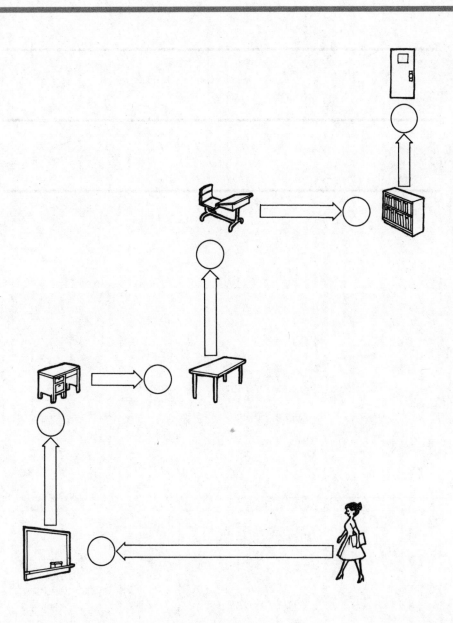

Lesson 95

winter	spring	summer	fall

_____

_____

_____

_____

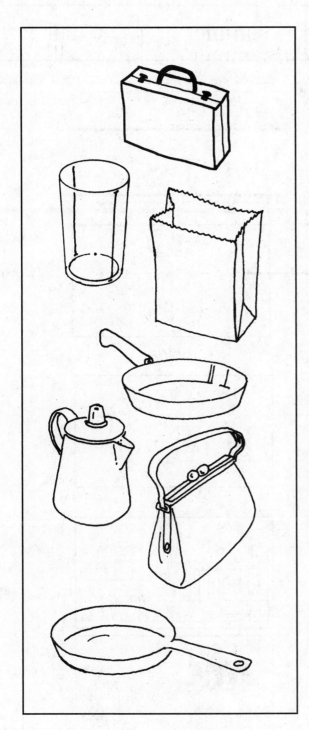

Lesson 96

Name _____

winter	spring	summer	fall

_____   _____

_____   _____

holds   **as**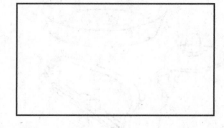

holds

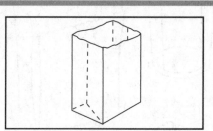

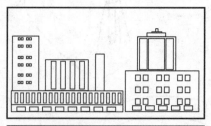

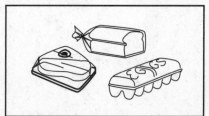

Lesson 97

Name _____

buildings	plants

_____   _____

_____   _____

_____   _____

_____   _____

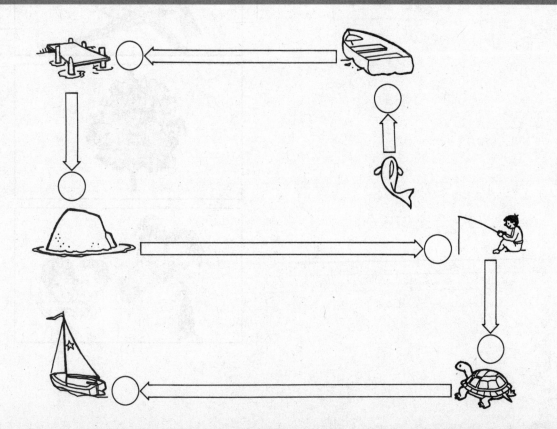

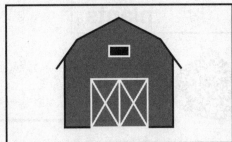

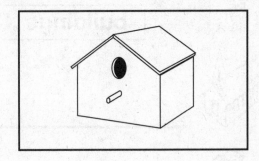

holds   **as**

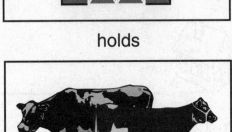

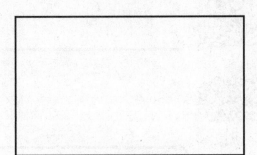

Lesson 98

Name _____

△ | **big** **win** **push** **smooth** **open** |

1. rough   _____   4. pull   _____

2. lose   _____   5. small   _____

3. shut   _____

| **containers**   **furniture** |

 _____   _____

 _____   _____

 _____   _____

Lesson 98

Name _____

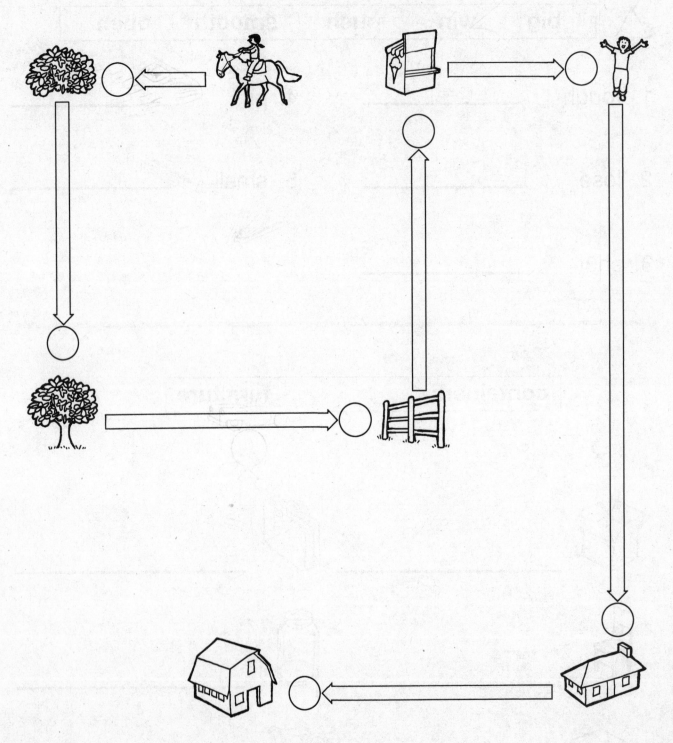

Name _____

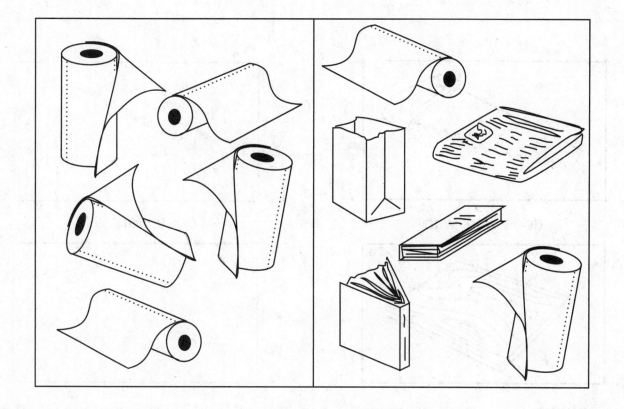

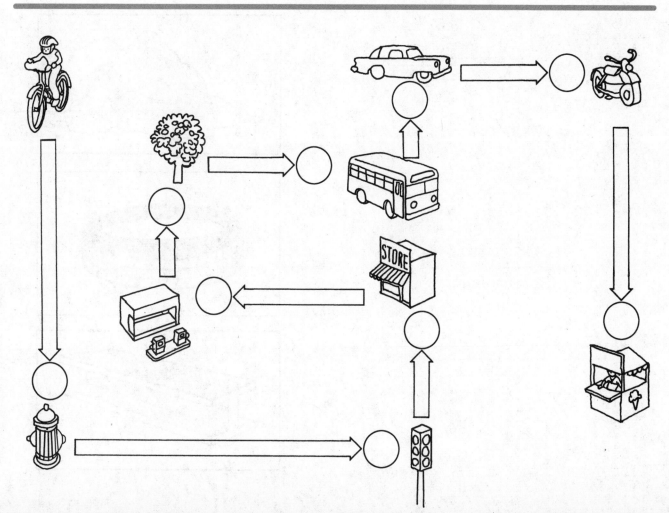

Lesson 99

Name _____

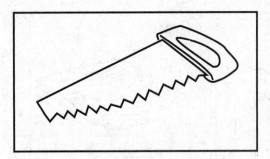

does work with

as

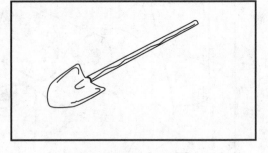

does work with

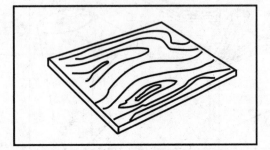

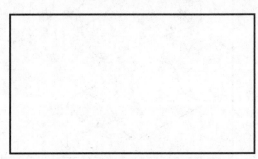

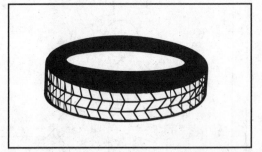

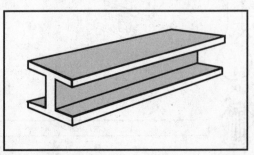

Lesson 100   Name _____

animals	vehicles

 _____   _____

_____   _____

 _____   _____

_____   _____

△ | **deep** | **easy** | **raw** | **clean** | **near** |

1. cooked _____   4. dirty _____

2. shallow _____   5. hard _____

3. far _____

Lesson 100

Name _____

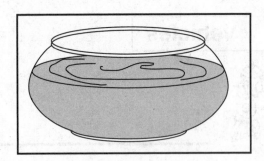

holds

as

holds

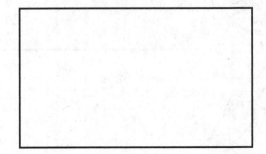

Lesson 101   Name _____

△ | **quiet** | **shallow** | **cooked** | **short** |

1. long _____

2. deep _____

3. loud _____

4. raw _____

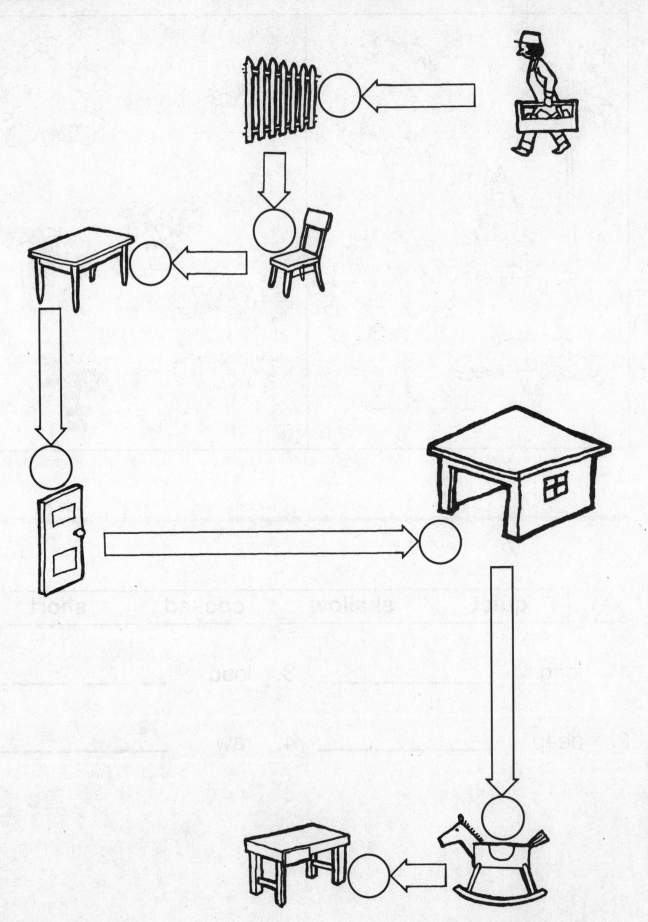

Lesson 102   Name _____

food	tools

  _____   _____

  _____   _____

🍴 _____

Sunday	Monday	Tuesday	Wednesday
Thursday	Friday		Saturday

_____

_____

_____

_____

_____

_____

_____

Lesson 102

Name _____

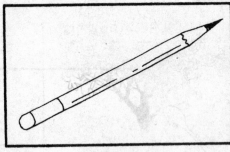

has

as

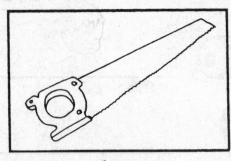

has

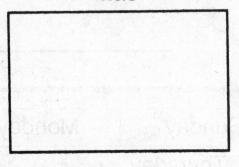

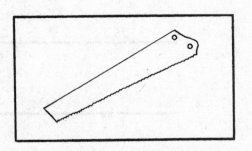

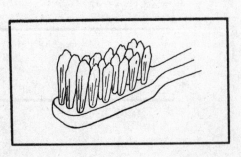

Lesson 103

Name _____

△ | **wide** | **shiny** | **pull** | **short** | **long** |

1. tall _____ 4. dull _____

2. push _____ 5. short _____

3. narrow _____

Lesson 103

Name _____

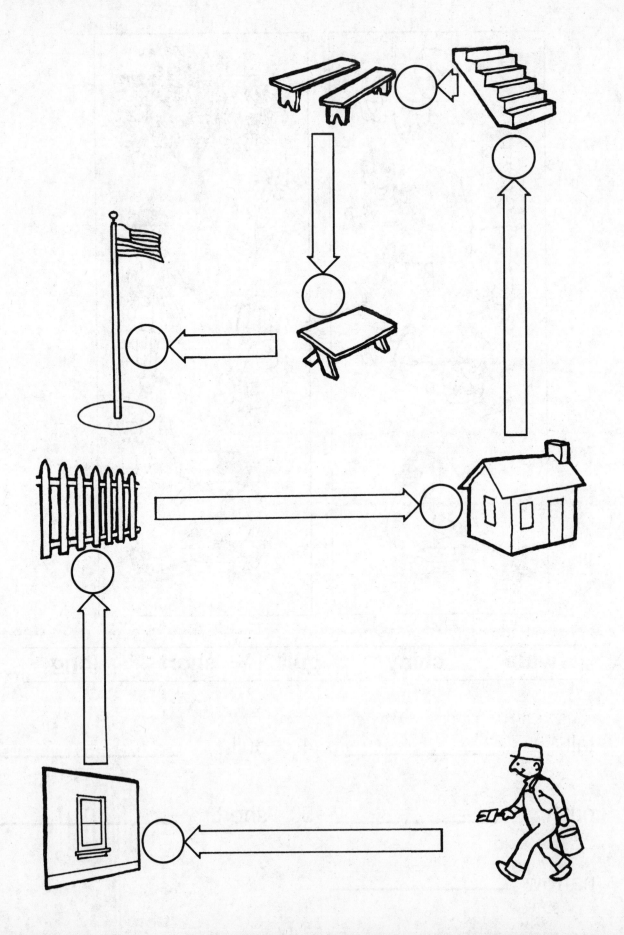

Lesson 104

Name _____

January, February, March ➡️

January
February

April, May, June ➡️

April

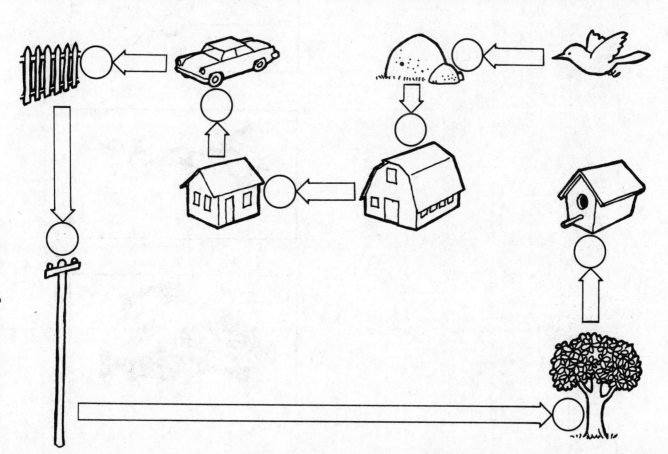

Lesson 104

Name _____

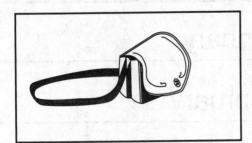

holds　　**as**　　holds

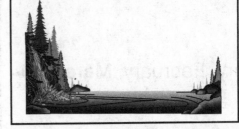

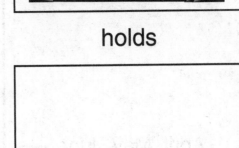

Lesson 105

Name _____

furniture   plants

 _____

 _____

 _____

 _____

 _____

Lesson 105   Name _____

△ | **cry**   **short**   **difficult**   **wide**   **dark**

1. easy _____   4. narrow _____

2. laugh _____   5. tall _____

3. light _____

January, February, March ➡ | January _____

February _____

April, May, June ➡ | April _____

_____

Name _____

January, February, March ➡️

January
_____
_____

April, May, June ➡️

_____
_____
_____

clothing   buildings

 _____   _____

 _____   _____

 _____   _____

Lesson 106

Name _____

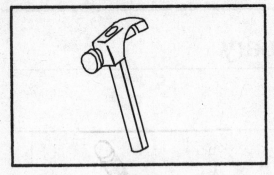

has

as

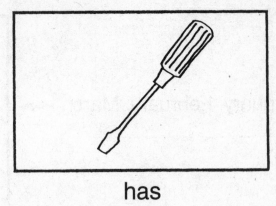

has

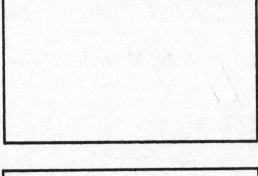

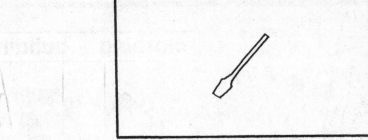

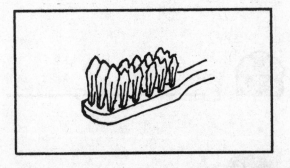

Name _____

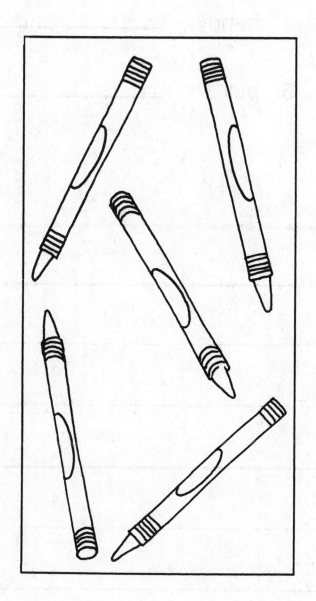

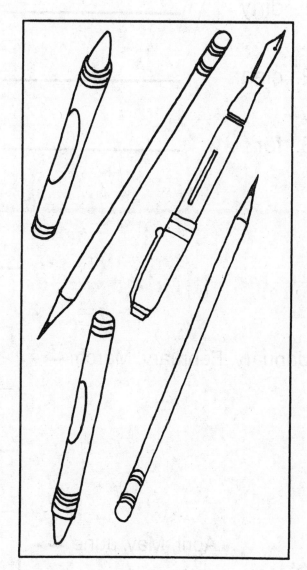

Lesson 107   Name _____

△ | sad   clean   push   near   dirty |

1. dirty _____   4. happy _____

2. clean _____   5. pull _____

3. far _____

January, February, March ➡ _____
_____

April, May, June ➡ _____
_____

Lesson 108　　　　Name _____

△ | **open** | **happy** | **big** | **weak** | **shiny** |

1. small _____   4. strong _____

2. shut _____   5. sad _____

3. dull _____

| winter | spring | summer | fall |

_____

_____

_____

_____

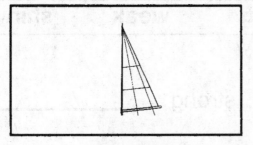   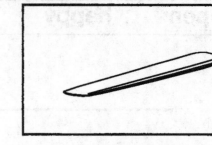

belongs   **as**   belongs

Name _____

vehicles	containers

_____   _____

                    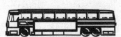

_____   _____

_____   _____

_____   _____

Lesson 109

Name _____

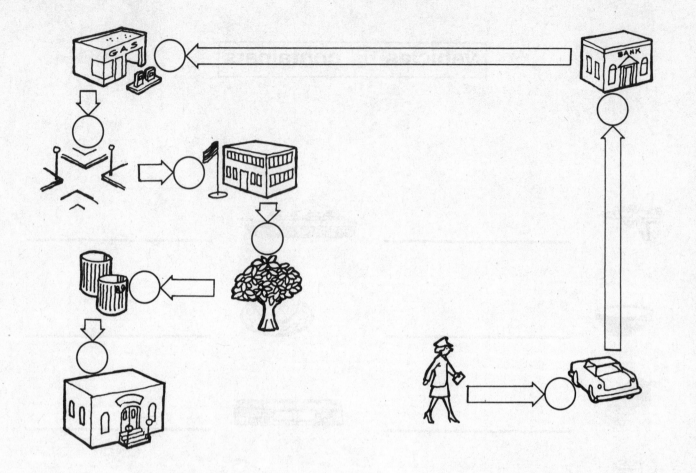

January, February, March ➡

April, May, June ➡

has

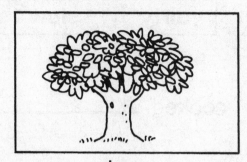

as

has

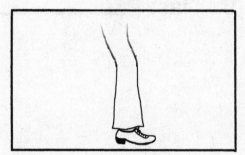

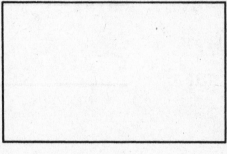

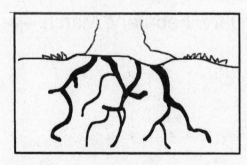

Lesson 110   Name _____

△ | **dirty**　**slow**　**raw**　**dark**　**skinny** |

1. cooked _____

2. light _____

3. fat _____

4. clean _____

5. fast _____

January, February, March ➙

_____
_____

April, May, June ➙

_____
_____

Lesson 111 Name _____

| rough | young | push | smooth | old | pull |

1. The ice was very smooth.

_____

2. One old tree is next to the house.

_____

January, February, March ➞

_____

_____

April, May, June ➞

_____

_____

July, August, September ➞

_____

September

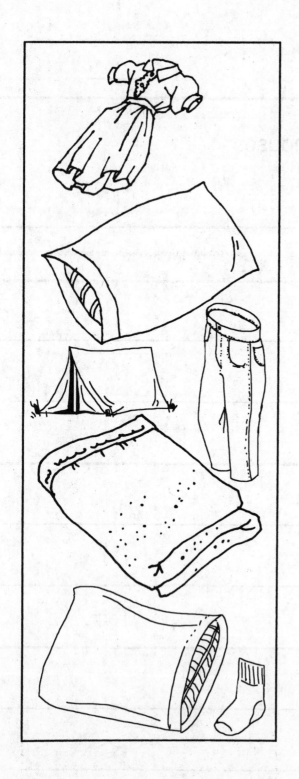

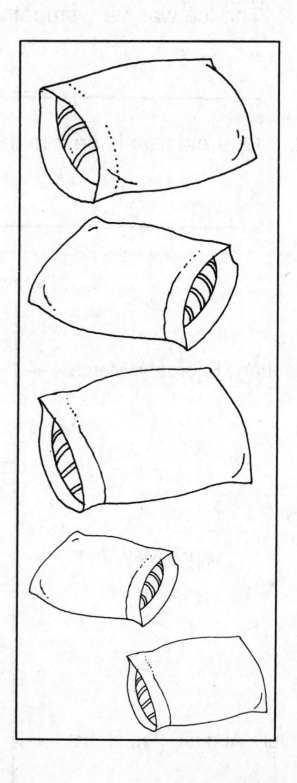

Lesson 112 Name _____

1. There were wet clothes on the line.

_____

2. The horse was fast.

_____

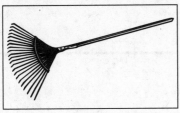 has **as**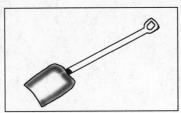

has

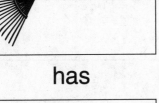

January, February, March ➡

April, May, June ➡

July, August, September ➡

September

Lesson 113   Name _____

containers	animals

 _____   _____

 _____    _____

 _____   _____

 _____   _____

January, February, March ➡

_____

_____

April, May, June ➡

_____

_____

July, August, September ➡

_____

_____

Lesson 113   Name _____

Sunday	Monday	Tuesday	Wednesday
Thursday		Friday	Saturday

_____

_____

_____

_____

_____

_____

_____

Lesson 114   Name _____

| deep | quiet | noisy | raw | shallow | cooked |

1. The children were quiet.

_____

2. The water was deep.

_____

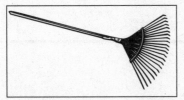   

does work with   **as**   does work with

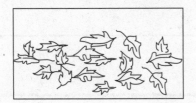   

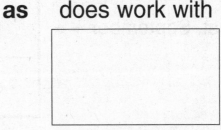

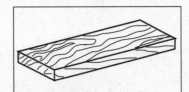

Lesson 114   Name _____

January, February, March ➝

_____

_____

April, May, June ➝

_____

_____

July, August, September ➝

_____

_____

Lesson 115

Name _____

		True	False
1.	Tables have legs.		
2.	Water is wet.		
3.	Birds have feet.		

vehicles	food

 _____    _____

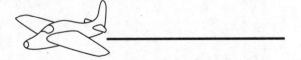 _____   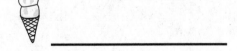 _____

 _____    _____

 _____    _____

Lesson 115   Name _____

January, February, March ➡

April, May, June ➡

July, August, September ➡

Lesson 116

Name _____

	True	**False**

1. A tree grows in the clouds. _____

2. The sun shines at night. _____

3. A plant is a vehicle. _____

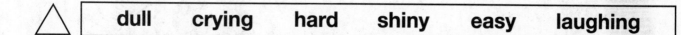

△ | dull   crying   hard   shiny   easy   laughing |

1. Is that girl crying?

   _____

2. We were done with that hard job.

   _____

Lesson 116

Name _____

has

as

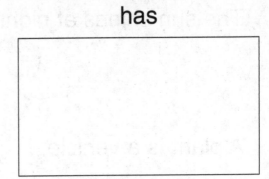

has

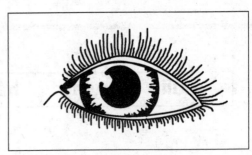

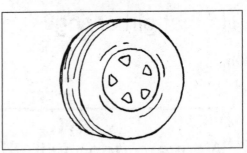

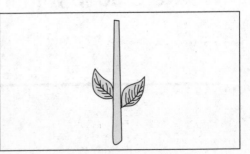

True   **False**

1.   A plant is a vehicle.   _____

2.   Glasses are made of wood.   _____

3.   A horse can walk.   _____

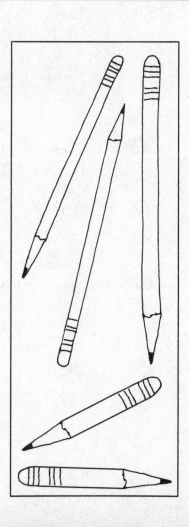

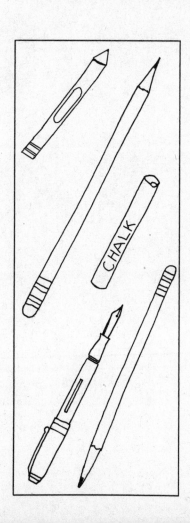

Lesson 117   Name _____

winter	spring	summer	fall

_____

_____

_____

_____

Lesson 118   Name _____

△ | **deep   cooked   easy   shallow   hard   raw**

1. The fish was raw.

_____

2. The bowl was shallow.

_____

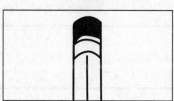

has

as

has

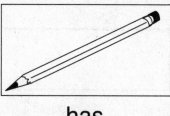

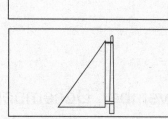

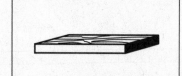

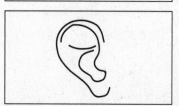

Lesson 118 Name ____________________

January, February, March →

April, May, June →

July, August, September →

October, November, December → October

Lesson 119

Name _____

		True	False
1.	A dog barks.		_____
2.	People eat vehicles.		_____
3.	You sweep with a broom.		_____

---

tools	furniture	plants

 _____

 _____

 _____

 _____

 _____

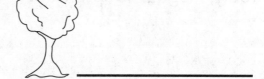 _____

 _____

 _____

 _____

Name _____

January, February, March ➡️

April, May, June ➡️

July, August, September ➡️

October, November, December ➡️

Lesson 120   Name _____

	True	**False**
1. A train is furniture.	_____	
2. You can read a bicycle.	_____	
3. People smell with ears.	_____	

△ | **wide** **empty** **dull** **narrow** **shiny** **full**

1. We went down a narrow street.

_____

2. The old pot was dull.

_____

Lesson 120

Name _____

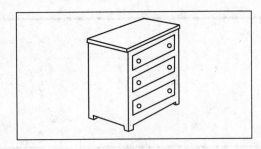

has

as

has

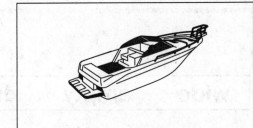

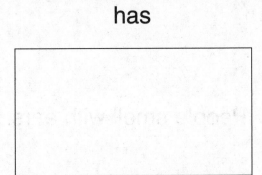

Lesson 121   Name _____

	True	**False**
1. Ice is cold.		_____
2. Cats have feet.		_____
3. Fish climb trees.		_____

△ | **short**   **pull**   **clean**   **push**   **tall**   **dirty**

1. I am going to push the wagon.

_____

2. My hands are dirty.

_____

3. She is as short as her sister.

_____

Name _____

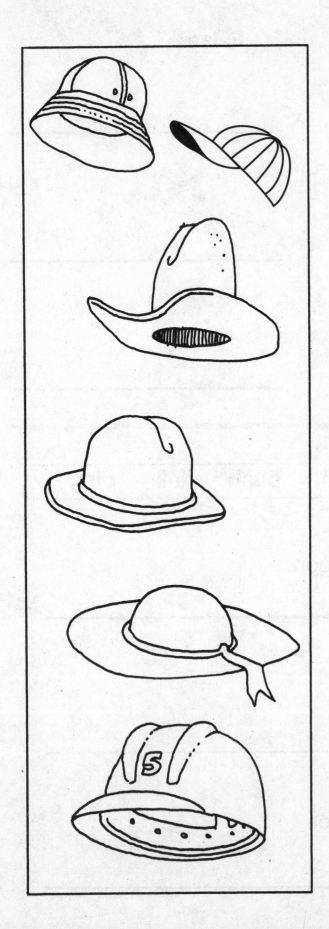

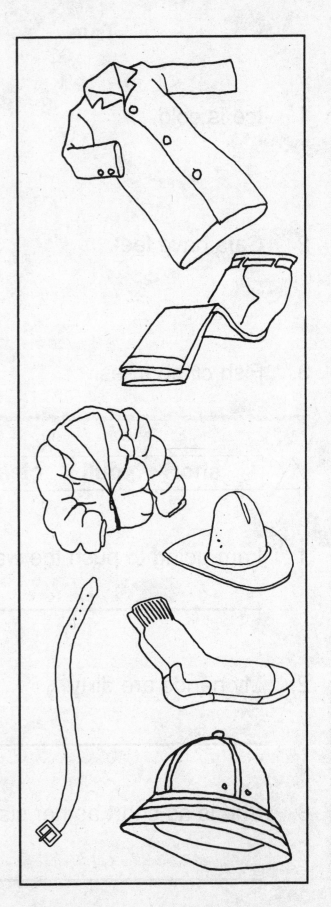

Lesson 122   Name _____

True   **False**

1. A book is made of paper.   _____

2. Ice cream is cold.   _____

3. A bed is furniture.   _____

△ | **old**   **nighttime**   **young**   **soft**   **hard**   **daytime**

1. I don't like soft beds.

_____

2. She ate during the nighttime.

_____

3. My dog is old.

_____

Sunday	Monday	Tuesday	Wednesday
Thursday		Friday	Saturday

_____

_____

_____

_____

_____

_____

_____

Lesson 123

Name _____

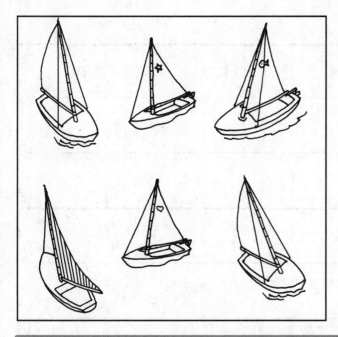

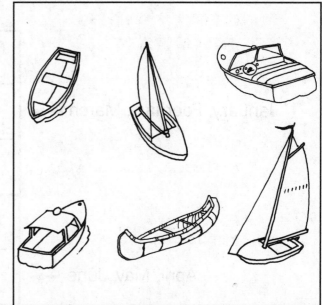

has **as** has

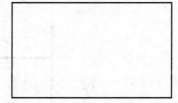

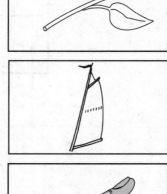

Lesson 123

Name _____

January, February, March ➞

April, May, June ➞

July, August, September ➞

October, November, December ➞

Lesson 124 Name _____

	True	**False**

1. A bottle is a plant. _____

2. Lamps give light. _____

3. The moon grows in the ground. _____

△ | **noisy** **late** **well** **quiet** **early** **sick** |

1. The birds were noisy.

_____

2. We got up very early.

_____

3. Her mother is sick.

_____

Lesson 124   Name _____

January, February, March ➡

_____

_____

April, May, June ➡

_____

_____

July, August, September ➡

_____

_____

October, November, December ➡

_____

_____

Lesson 125

Name _____

	True	**False**
1.	People eat vehicles.	_____
2.	A table is furniture.	_____
3.	A saw is made of paper.	_____

vehicles	colors	plants

truck _____   weed _____

tree _____   pink _____

ship _____   yellow _____

green _____   grass _____

van _____   red _____

Lesson 125   Name _____

January, February, March ➤
_____
_____

April, May, June ➤
_____
_____

July, August, September ➤
_____
_____

October, November, December ➤
_____
_____

Lesson 126 Name _____

△ | **sad** | **fast** | **happy** | **cold** | **slow** | **hot** |

1. She is a happy kitty.

_____

2. Jim is a fast runner.

_____

3. Hot water is in the sink.

_____

| winter | spring | summer | fall |

_____

_____

_____

Lesson 126

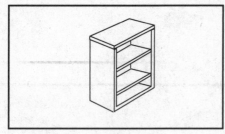

has

as

has

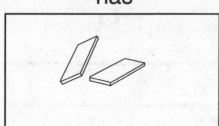

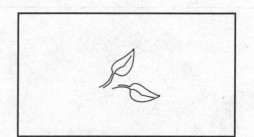

Lesson 127

Name _____

	True	**False**
1. You wear shoes on your head.		_____
2. A box is a building.		_____
3. An airplane goes in the air.		_____

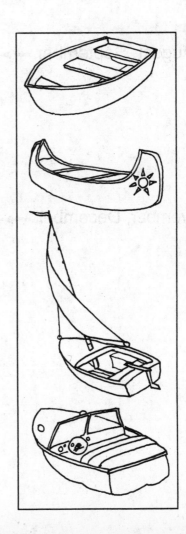

Lesson 127   Name _____

January, February, March ➝

April, May, June ➝

July, August, September ➝

October, November, December ➝

Lesson 128   Name _____

	True	**False**

1. Chickens give milk.   _____

2. You eat clothing.   _____

3. You can ride on a horse.   _____

△ | **full   empty   big   small   long   short**

1. The big bike is mine.

_____

2. She had a long pencil.

_____

3. His cup is full.

_____

Lesson 128   Name _____

January, February, March →

_____

_____

April, May, June →

_____

_____

July, August, September →

_____

_____

October, November, December →

_____

_____

Lesson 129

Name _____

food	clothing	animals

nuts _____   goat _____

coat _____   cake _____

cat _____   dress _____

pants _____   shirt _____

---

large	yell	little	shout	big	small

1. I will yell at the dog.

   _____

2. I found a small bottle.

   _____

3. That house is big.

   _____

Lesson 129   Name _____

Sunday	Monday	Tuesday	Wednesday
Thursday		Friday	Saturday

_____

_____

_____

_____

_____

_____

_____

has   **as**   has

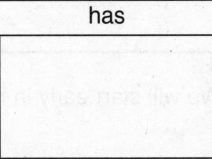

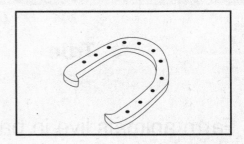

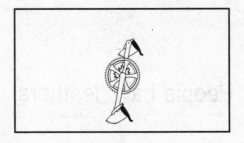

△ | **hot**   **cold**   **late**   **early**   **clean**   **dirty**

1.   The pan felt too cold.

   _____

2.   We will start early in the day.

   _____

3.   He always has a clean car.

   _____

	True	**False**

1.   Farm animals live in barns.   _____

2.   People have feathers.   _____

3.   You find the moon in the sky.   _____

Lesson 131   Name _____

over	shut	cry	close	above	weep

1. Ask Jim to shut the window.

_____

2. Hold your hands over your head.

_____

3. My little brother will weep.

_____

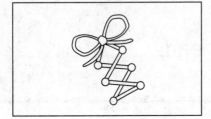

has   **as**   has

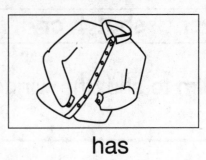

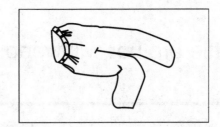

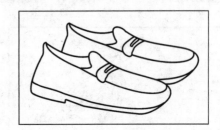

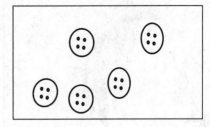

Lesson 132   Name _____

| close   well   fast   healthy   quick   shut |

1.   The cat is very fast.

   _____

2.   Your dad looks healthy.

   _____

3.   Shut your eyes.

   _____

Lesson 132   Name _____

△ | **raw cooked shallow deep dangerous safe**

1. He walked in a dangerous place.

   _____

2. She played in shallow water.

   _____

3. Most of the food was raw.

   _____

                True   **False**

1. A boat has wheels. _____

2. A boat has roots. _____

3. A table is furniture. _____

Lesson 133

Name _____

bright thin shiny hard skinny difficult

1. The pot was bright.

_____

2. That trick is hard.

_____

3. Her dog looks thin.

_____

has

as

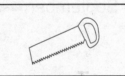

has

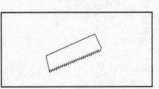

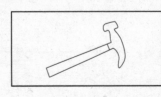

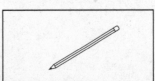

Lesson 133

Name _____

January, February, March ➡
_____
_____

April, May, June ➡
_____
_____

July, August, September ➡
_____
_____

October, November, December ➡
_____
_____

Lesson 134   Name _____

| big | shout | large | yell | same | alike |

1. Why will that girl yell?

_____

2. Those two dogs looked alike.

_____

3. The clown had large feet.

_____

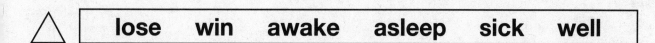

△ | lose | win | awake | asleep | sick | well |

1. The baby is awake.

_____

2. He has been well for a week.

_____

3. I think his team will win the game.

_____

Lesson 134   Name _____

winter	spring	summer	fall

_____

_____

_____

_____

True	**False**

1.   You use a fork when you eat.   _____

2.   People live in restaurants.   _____

3.   A box is a building.   _____

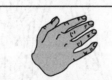

belongs to   **as**   belongs to

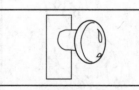

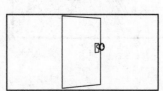

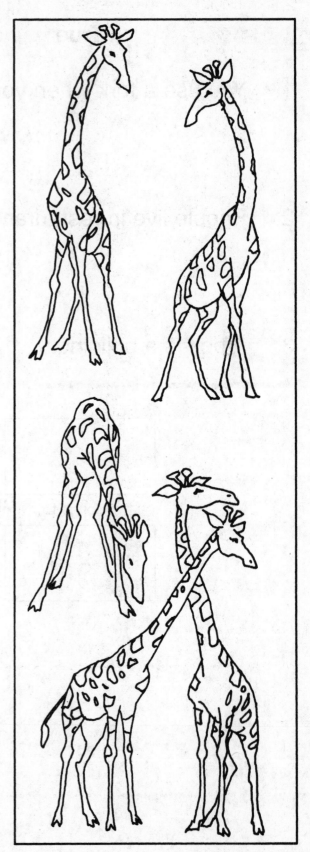

Lesson 136   Name _____

close   near   happy   shut   glad   closed

1. Stay close to the road.

    _____

2. The teacher closed the door.

    _____

3. Why do they feel glad?

    _____

Lesson 136   Name _____

| old | young | open | close | late | early |

1. We got there too early.

_____

2. Open that door for me.

_____

3. My brother is old.

_____

          True   **False**

1. Scissors can cut cloth.   _____

2. A blanket is made of cloth.   _____

3. A barn is furniture.   _____

Lesson 137   Name _____

<table>
<tr><th align="center">True</th><th align="center">False</th></tr>
</table>

1.   Snow is hot.   _____

2.   You go to school to learn.   _____

3.   A dress is made of cloth.   _____

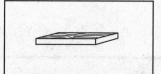

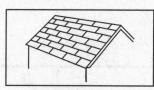

belongs to   **as**   belongs to

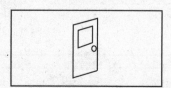

Lesson 137

Name _____

Sunday	Monday	Tuesday	Wednesday
Thursday		Friday	Saturday

_____

_____

_____

_____

_____

_____

_____

Lesson 138   Name _____

	containers	numbers	tools

jar _____   six _____

saw _____   bag _____

ten _____   rake _____

cup _____   three _____

mop _____   nine _____

Lesson 138   Name _____

△ | **old   young   late   early   open   close**

1. Who will open the back door?

    _____

2. I think we're going to get there early.

    _____

3. That horse looks old.

    _____

---

hard   weep   quick   cry   difficult   fast

1. The snow made walking hard.

    _____

2. Her fingers were quick.

    _____

3. She might weep.

    _____

| little | difficult | thin | small | hard | skinny |

1. Our cat has little spots.

_____

2. Those birds look skinny.

_____

3. That work is getting hard.

_____

	True	**False**

1. A hammer is a tool.   _____

2. You wear shoes on your hands. _____

3. A hat is a building.   _____

belongs to   **as**   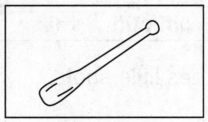 belongs to

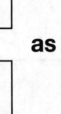

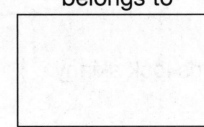

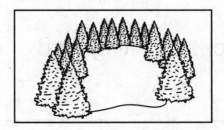

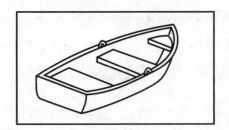

Lesson 140   Name _____

△ | **tall   short   full   empty   hot   cold** |

1.   The soup was too hot.

_____

2.   My uncle is very tall.

_____

3.   The gas tank is almost empty.

_____

_____

True   **False**

1.   Snakes have legs.   _____

2.   Hairbrushes are used to brush hair.   _____

3.   You eat clothing.   _____

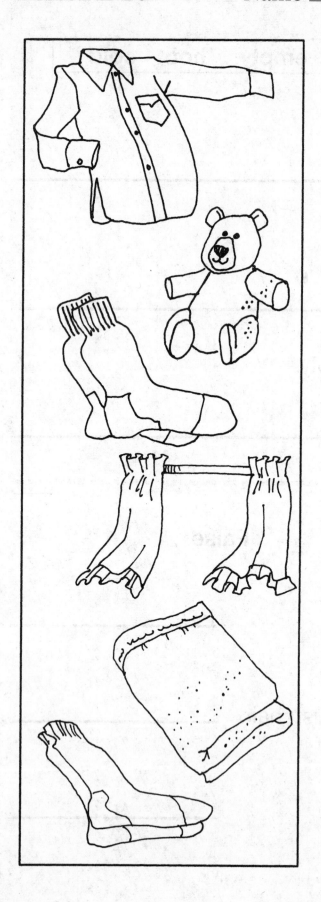

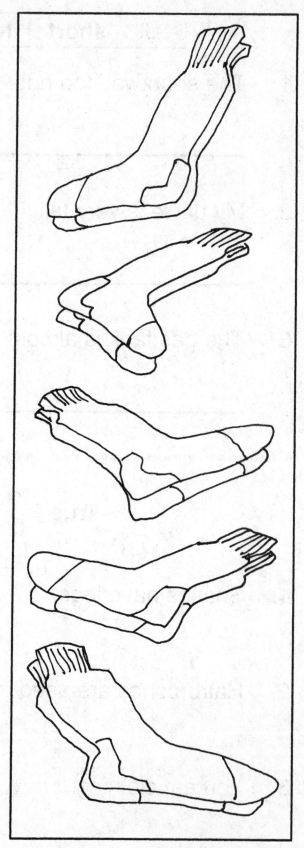

Lesson 141

bright	fast	shiny	above	over	quick

1. Her ring was a bright blue.

   _____

2. The window was above the door.

   _____

3. She was a quick eater.

   _____

_____

	True	**False**

1. A doll is a tool. _____

2. Dogs have wings. _____

3. A hammer is a tool. _____

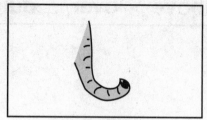

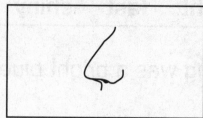

is part of   **as**   is part of

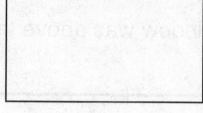

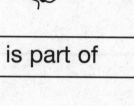

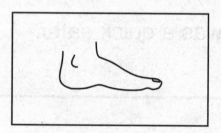

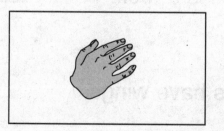

Lesson 142   Name _____

| wet | dry | awake | asleep | hard | soft |

△

1. The snow was very soft.

   _____

2. My coat is getting dry.

   _____

3. Is the baby still awake?

   _____

_____

           True   **False**

1. Fish swim in water.   _____

2. Eggs come from chickens. _____

3. Ice is hot.   _____

Sunday	Monday	Tuesday	Wednesday
Thursday		Friday	Saturday

_____

_____

_____

_____

_____

_____

Name _____

| below | healthy | under | big | large | well |

1. They live in a large house.

    _____

2. He was not healthy last year.

    _____

3. A cave was below the road.

    _____

True   **False**

1. A window has a frame.   _____

2. A window is made of glass.   _____

3. Cats have windows.   _____

Lesson 143

Name _____

belong to **as** belong to

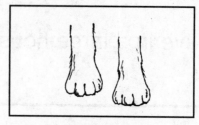

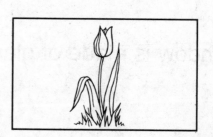

Lesson 144 Name _____

1. They love to eat raw carrots.

_____

2. That party made me feel sad.

_____

3. He's a strong boy.

_____

                True   **False**

1. You can put things in a container. _____

2. An apple is a container. _____

3. A cup is a container. _____

Lesson 144   Name _____

January, February, March ➡

_____
_____

April, May, June ➡

_____
_____

July, August, September ➡

_____
_____

October, November, December ➡

_____
_____

Lesson 145

Name _____

△ | **shiny   dull   dangerous   safe   rough   smooth** |

1. Is that beach safe for children?

    _____

2. His car was always dull.

    _____

3. Fox Road is as smooth as Red Road.

    _____

| **vehicles   animals   clothing** |

sock   _____   turtle   _____

boat   _____   tractor _____

shark _____   horse   _____

hat   _____   dress   _____

train _____   car   _____

Lesson 145

Name _____

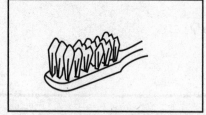

belong to **as** belong to

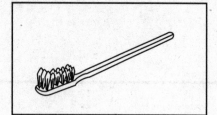

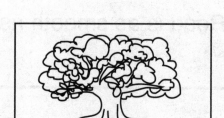

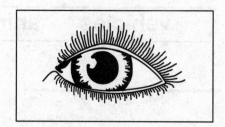

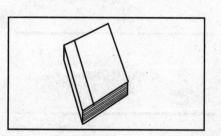

Name _____

Lesson 148

Name _____

P	Pink rocks	
B	Brown rocks	
G	Gray rocks	
	Other rocks	

Name _____

	Red birds	
	Yellow birds	
	Blue birds	
	Other animals	

Name _____